fascinating+real
BODIES REVEALED

With deep appreciation to
those who donated their bodies
so that others may learn

INTRODU

People, from time immemorial, have studied and written about the human body. Aristotle, Plato, Hippocrates, Cicero, Galen, Vesalius, Fabricius, Descartes, and Harvey represent a Who's Who of some of the greatest minds who have devoted their talents to this study. And to this list we should not forget to add famous artists like da Vinci, Titian, Michelangelo, Raphael, and Rembrandt, all of whom made significant contributions to our understanding of the human form by combining artistic ability with keen observation.

Why all this interest in the human body? The answer to this question seems quite clear to me: your body is the only thing you carry with you from the moment you are born until your very last breath. Knowledge of one's body, its structure (how it is put together) and its function (how it works), represents some of the most practical, useful information a person could possibly want to possess.

CTION

If this is something we can agree on, then how does one explain why so many people today are basically still infants when it comes to an understanding of their own bodies? Too many people abuse their bodies by getting far too little sleep, by eating far too much of the wrong food, by getting far too little exercise, by taking far too many drugs, and by drinking far more alcohol than their bodies can tolerate. And, we also know that these abuses carry with them some very significant and serious consequences. It is widely reported in the national press that too many people are overweight, that many preventable medical conditions, such as heart disease and certain forms of cancer are on the increase, and that the already exorbitant costs of medical insurance and hospital care continue to rise. Today it seems that the best medicine anyone could possibly prescribe to get at the root cause of these problems is a good dose of body education.

Just as students who prepare themselves for a career in medicine are required to dissect and study the human body in order to understand its complexities, why can't the average person do much the same thing, if provided with a similar learning experience? This extraordinary Exhibition—*Bodies Revealed*—was designed with that one important purpose in mind: education.

The bodies and organs that you will be looking at are real. Unlike models that idealize the body through the eyes of an artist, the specimens in this Exhibition will show you the body and its parts the way they really are. And, as I've discovered in my more than 30 years of teaching anatomy to medical students, seeing promotes understanding and understanding promotes the most practical kind of body education possible.

How were the specimens on display in our Exhibition obtained and prepared? All of the bodies and organs came from individuals who chose to donate their bodies to medical science for the purpose of study and education. They were then preserved using a process called polymer preservation. In this process, tissue water is first removed by submersion in acetone. Then the acetone, too, is removed in a vacuum chamber. During this step in the process, known as impregnation, the tissue spaces within the specimen, formerly filled with acetone, become filled instead with liquid silicone

rubber. Lastly, during a step called curing, the silicone rubber is treated with a catalyst and hardened. The end product is a rubberized specimen that can be easily examined without any chance of it deteriorating due to the natural decay that otherwise would have rendered it unfit for study or public view.

So, in light of all that I've just said, my advice to you is simple. Enjoy your visit to our Exhibition. Join the long list of men and women who throughout the centuries have been amazed by the beauty and the complexity of the human body. Look and be amazed yourself by the complexity of its many bones, muscles, nerves, and blood vessels. Look into the heart, into the brain, into the intestine, into the lungs, and leave the Exhibition with a better understanding of how your body works.

Opening yourself to a greater knowledge of your own body will enable you to make more informed decisions about its care and keeping. If you are successful at doing this, then the countless hours of work that have gone into developing and preparing the Exhibition for you to enjoy will have been richly rewarded.

Dr. Roy Glover, Medical Director
Professor Emeritus
Anatomy and Cell Biology
University of Michigan

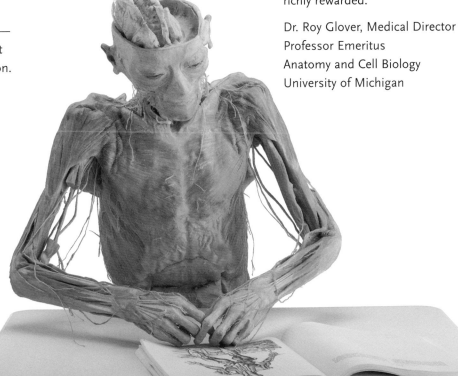

Each of us is physically unique, from the shade of our skin to the size and shape of our organs. What we have in common is a miraculous set of organ systems, each with their own precise role in how we function. The *Bodies Revealed* Exhibition is designed to look deep inside those systems. Using authentic human bodies and individual organ specimens, what was once a mystery, accessible only to the medical profession, is now available for all to see. To quote Albert Einstein, "The most beautiful thing we can experience is the mysterious...."

This first full body specimen, "The Body Revealed," serves as an example of the relationship these systems have to each other as they supervise our bodies.

SKELETAL SYSTEM

The bones of the skeletal system comprise the body's internal framework. This specimen reveals every type of bone in the body: long bones (arms and legs); flat bones (ribs and skull); short bones (wrists and ankles); irregular bones (spine); and sesamoid bones, found in a location where a tendon passes over a joint (metacarpal bones of the hand).

MUSCULAR SYSTEM

Muscles give the body much of its individual shape and generate heat to help maintain its optimal temperature. When a muscle contracts it shortens, pulling bones together, causing movement at the joint it crosses. For example, the biceps brachii muscle of the arm crosses joints at the shoulder and the elbow. Its contraction can cause movement at one or both of these joints.

NERVOUS SYSTEM

The brain and spinal cord make up the central nervous system (CNS). All the nerves that branch from the brain and spinal cord are known as the peripheral nervous system (PNS). Together these systems monitor and manage every activity of the body. The countless number of nerves in the PNS continually send information from the body, via sensory nerves, to the CNS, which processes that information and sends the appropriate response, via motor nerves, back to the voluntary skeletal muscles. The autonomic nervous system, a division of the PNS, controls the involuntary activities of the body such as the beating of the heart.

DIGESTIVE SYSTEM

The size of the abdominal cavity illustrates the importance of our digestive system. Approximately twenty-five feet long (7.6 meters), our digestive system converts the foods we eat into the fuel our bodies use to perform all vital functions.

RESPIRATORY SYSTEM

The lungs are made of soft spongy tissue that expands as you breathe. When you inhale, air enters the lungs, filling the 300 million alveoli (air sacs) at the end of the airways. In the alveoli, the body absorbs oxygen from the outside air and releases carbon dioxide. Carbon dioxide is exhaled and the absorbed oxygen is transported via the blood to every cell in the body.

CIRCULATORY SYSTEM

The adult circulatory system is made up of the heart and 100,000 miles of blood vessels (161,000 kilometers). The aorta supplies the lower half of the body with oxygenated blood. It is visible in the mid-section of this specimen, close to the spine. The larger blood vessel to the right of the aorta is the inferior vena cava. It is the primary vein by which blood from the lower limbs returns to the heart.

REPRODUCTIVE SYSTEM

Unique to men, the testes produce sperm, the male sex cell. In women, the ovaries make the ovum (egg), the female sex cell. When the sperm and egg join together, fertilization occurs and a cell called a zygote is created.

URINARY SYSTEM

This system includes the ureters, the bladder, the urethra, and the primary organs of the system—the kidneys. The kidneys lie within the abdominal cavity where they are slightly offset because of the liver's location. They produce urine, the fluid by which the body rids itself of its harmful waste material, which is stored in the bladder until eliminated through the urethra. The urinary bladder, surrounded by the pelvic bones, can store over 1.5 pints (600 milliliters) of urine before needing to be emptied.

INTEGUMENTARY SYSTEM

The skin is the body's largest sense receptor and heaviest organ system. It protects us from extremes of temperature and invading organisms. It also contains hair follicles, sweat glands, and fingerprints—small ridges that assist our fingertips in handling very delicate materials.

THE BODY REVEALED

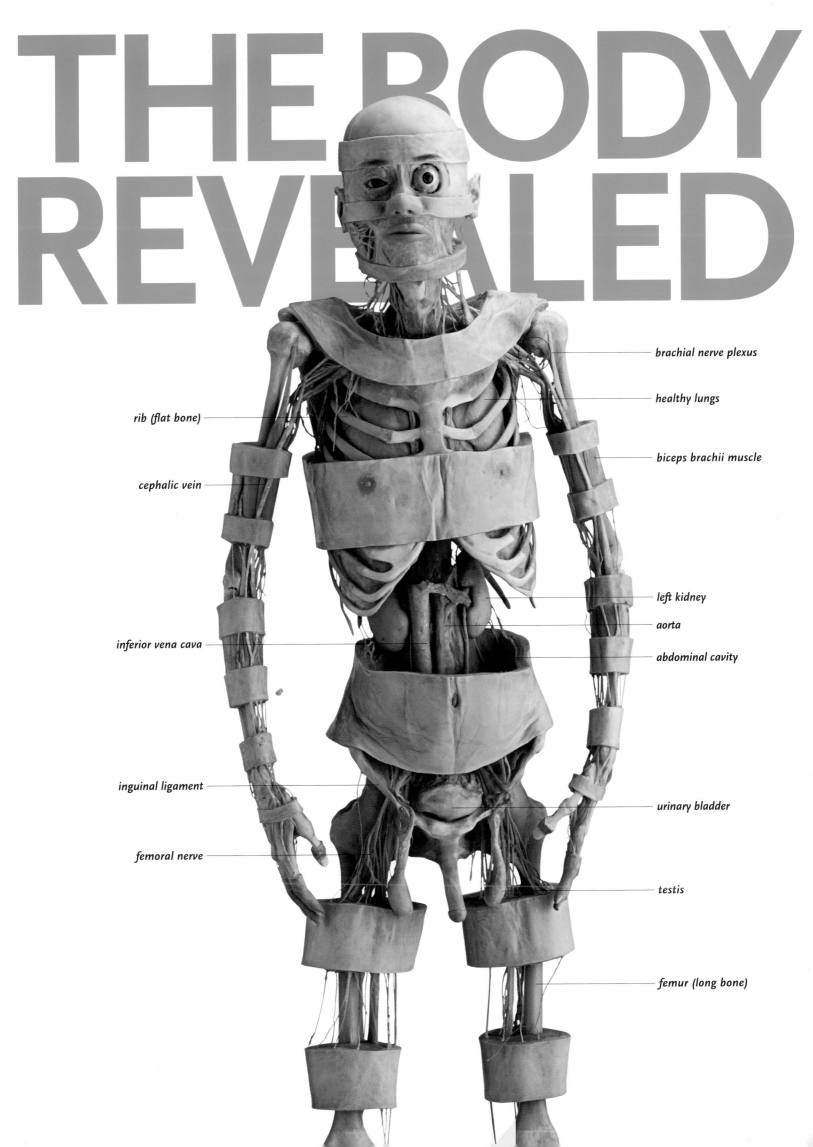

brachial nerve plexus

healthy lungs

rib (flat bone)

biceps brachii muscle

cephalic vein

left kidney

aorta

inferior vena cava

abdominal cavity

inguinal ligament

urinary bladder

femoral nerve

testis

femur (long bone)

SKELETAL

O f all the anatomical structures beneath our skins, we are most familiar with our skeletons. They are the subject of myth and legend and remain a visual reminder of our humanity long after our softer tissues have disappeared. Like the framework of a house, skeletons form the internal structure of our bodies, permitting us to resist the force of gravity, move through space, and carry our skins with dignity. They are a perfect combination of form and function: the S-shaped spine keeps the body upright and supports the head, while the pelvis balances the upper body over the feet.

Male and female skeletons are similar in nature. However, the female frame is usually lighter and smaller than the male frame, and includes a wider pelvis for childbirth.

Somewhat delicate in appearance, the bones in our skeletal system are actually four to five times stronger than mild steel, but make up only 14 percent of the body's total weight.

The skeleton derives its name from the Greek *skeletos*, which means dry. But the bones comprising the human skeleton are anything but dry; they are dynamic organisms that reinvent themselves in response to repeated stress and repair themselves when broken.

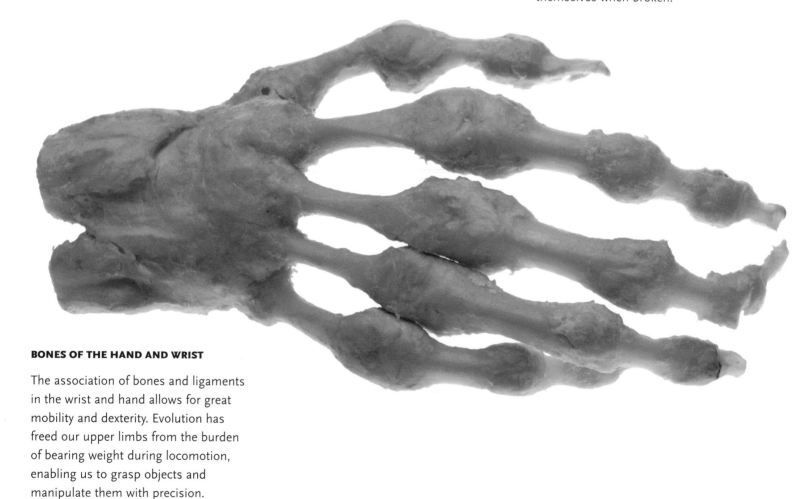

BONES OF THE HAND AND WRIST

The association of bones and ligaments in the wrist and hand allows for great mobility and dexterity. Evolution has freed our upper limbs from the burden of bearing weight during locomotion, enabling us to grasp objects and manipulate them with precision.

SYSTEM

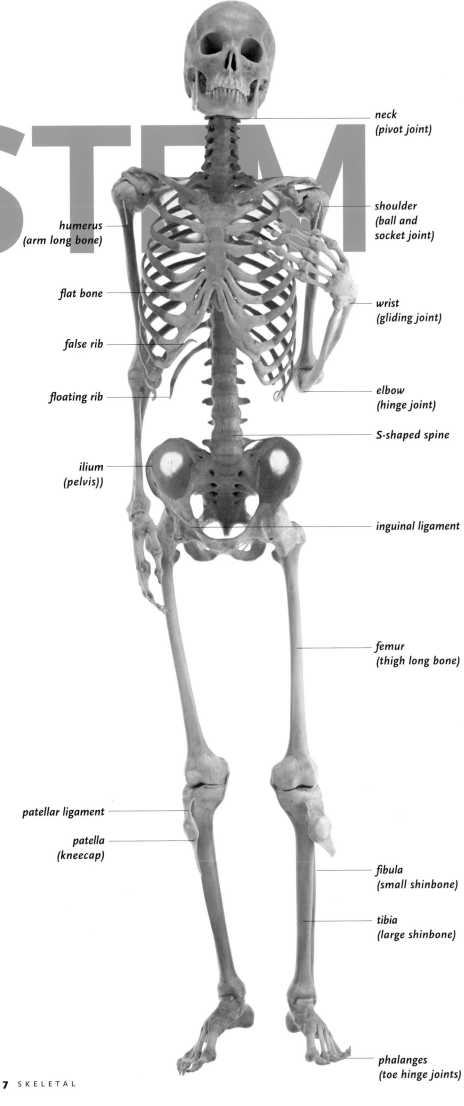

Made up of approximately 206 bones in an adult, our skeletons have multiple functions:

They protect our internal organs.

They store the calcium, minerals, and phosphorus ions necessary for their own strength and flexibility, and for proper nerve and muscle function.

They serve as anchors for our muscles, forming that one/two combination that gives the body action.

The marrow inside the flat bones and long bones of the adult skeletal system creates 2.5 million new red blood cells each second, facilitating the transfer of oxygen from our lungs to our tissues.

BONES, JOINTS, AND LIGAMENTS

Visible on this specimen are the bones, joints, and ligaments of the body.

Joints are the areas where our bones meet. They are classified by the range of movement they allow. For example, hinge joints (elbows, knees, fingers, and toes) allow the bones to swing in two directions, similar to the movement of a gate or door. Ball and socket joints (hip and shoulder) allow some rotation, as well as movement back and forth, and from side-to-side. Pivot joints (neck) facilitate a left to right movement similar to the course your head takes as it swivels on your spine.

Ligaments mainly connect bone to bone and prevent excessive movement that might cause dislocation or breakage of the bones that form a joint.

neck
(pivot joint)

shoulder
(ball and
socket joint)

humerus
(arm long bone)

wrist
(gliding joint)

flat bone

false rib

elbow
(hinge joint)

floating rib

S-shaped spine

ilium
(pelvis))

inguinal ligament

femur
(thigh long bone)

patellar ligament

patella
(kneecap)

fibula
(small shinbone)

tibia
(large shinbone)

phalanges
(toe hinge joints)

CARTILAGE AND DEEP MUSCLE

This dissection demonstrates the important relationship between the bones of our skeletons and the cartilage and muscle attached to these bones.

Cartilage is a tough and flexible connective tissue that allows bones to slide over one another at all moveable joints, reducing friction and preventing damage. If cartilage breaks down in the knees, pain and bone damage may result. Weakened cartilage in one of the back's vertebra might precipitate a slipped or crushed vertebral disc.

Lighter and more flexible than bone, cartilage strengthens non-weight-bearing parts of the body, like the nose and outer ears. Bend your ear toward your face and notice that when released, it instantly regains its original shape. It is the elasticity of cartilage that makes this possible.

Muscle and bone flow seamlessly together at every intersection of the body. Observe the areas surrounding the joints on this specimen.

The *biceps brachii muscle* on the arm attaches the humerus (arm bone) to the radius bone of our forearm, helping us to flex, and turn our palms upward.

The *pronator teres muscle* crosses the left elbow and also attaches to the radius bone. It allows us to turn our hands palms downward.

The *intercostal muscles* between the ribs are essential for breathing, as they make the chest into an airtight chamber.

The *iliopsoas muscles*, the wide bands of muscle that connect the lower back to the femur (thighbone), help us raise our knees.

The *gracilis muscle*, visible here on the right leg, is a long, strap-like muscle that acts to adduct the thigh and to flex the leg at the knee.

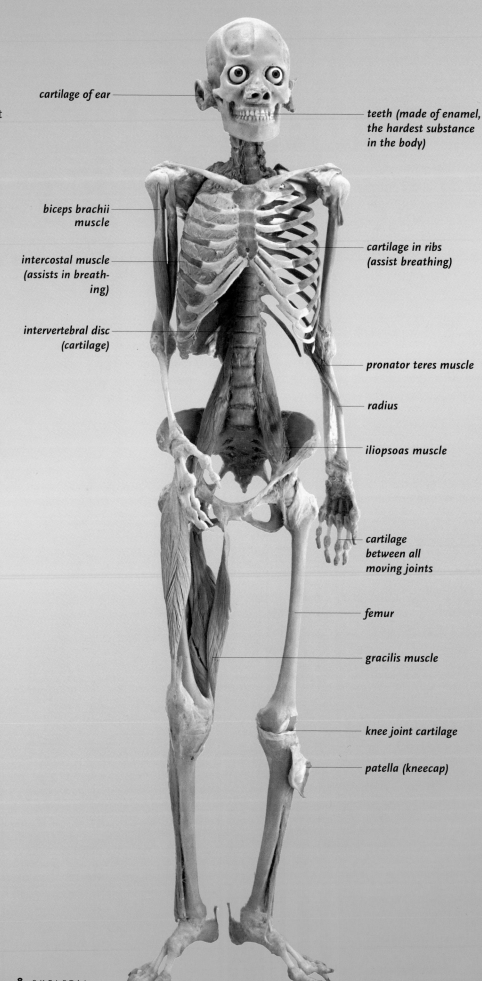

cartilage of ear

teeth (made of enamel, the hardest substance in the body)

biceps brachii muscle

cartilage in ribs (assist breathing)

intercostal muscle (assists in breathing)

intervertebral disc (cartilage)

pronator teres muscle

radius

iliopsoas muscle

cartilage between all moving joints

femur

gracilis muscle

knee joint cartilage

patella (kneecap)

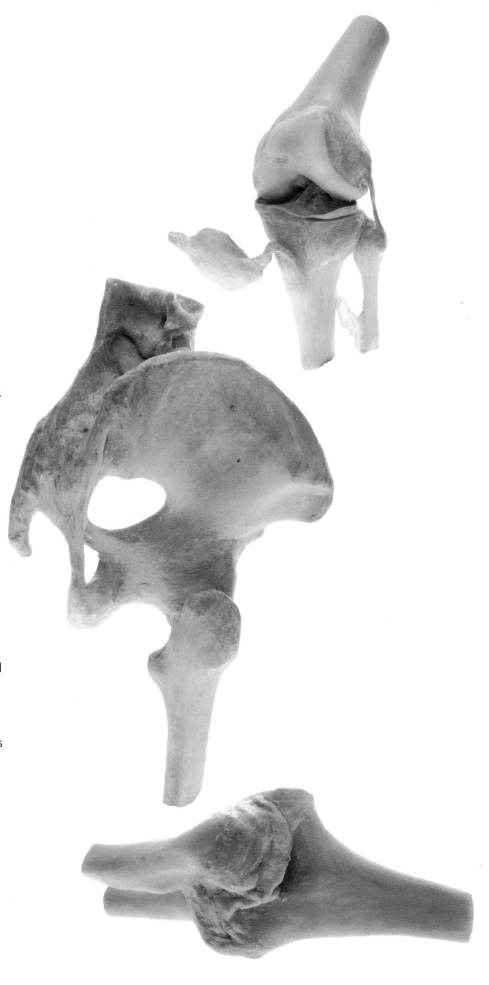

KNEE JOINT

This is the largest and most complex joint in the body and is primarily a hinge joint. It forms where the convex end of the femur (thighbone) meets the flattened, slightly concave end of the tibia (shinbone of the leg). The third bone of the knee, the patella (kneecap), is imbedded within the tendon of a powerful thigh muscle and acts to stabilize the knee by holding the femur and tibia together.

HIP JOINT

One of the strongest and most stable joints in the body, the hip joint (a ball and socket joint), is formed where the ball at the head of the femur fits into the acetabulum (socket) of the hipbone. This flexible joint structure allows for rotation, movement forward and backward, and from side-to-side. Held in place by five ligaments, as well as tough connective tissue deep in the joint, the hip joint is often called upon to withstand 400 pounds (180 kilograms) of force in everyday activity.

ELBOW JOINT

Formed by two bones, three ligaments, and fourteen muscles, the elbow joint permits flexion and extension of the forearm. This dissection shows the elbow encased within its articular capsule. The inner lining of this capsule forms the synovial membrane that produces synovial fluid, which provides lubrication for this hinge joint.

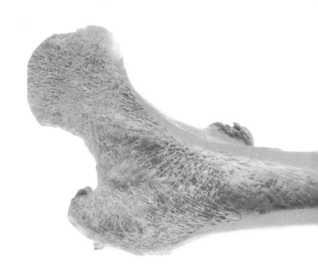

BONES: CONSTRUCTION, DISEASE, AND HEALING

Our hands and feet share a similar design, as you can see by comparing this foot with the hand on page six. Each hand has 27 bones; each foot has 26. The bones also have similar names (metacarpals and phalanges in the hand, metatarsals and phalanges in the foot). The tarsal bones at the back of the foot are comparable to the carpal bones of the wrist.

BONES OF THE FOOT AND ANKLE

The bones and ligaments of the foot and ankle provide support and stability by distributing the body's weight over a broad area. In addition, the connection between bones and ligaments creates an arch that, along with the powerful tendons in the ankle, allows the foot to conform to nearly any surface.

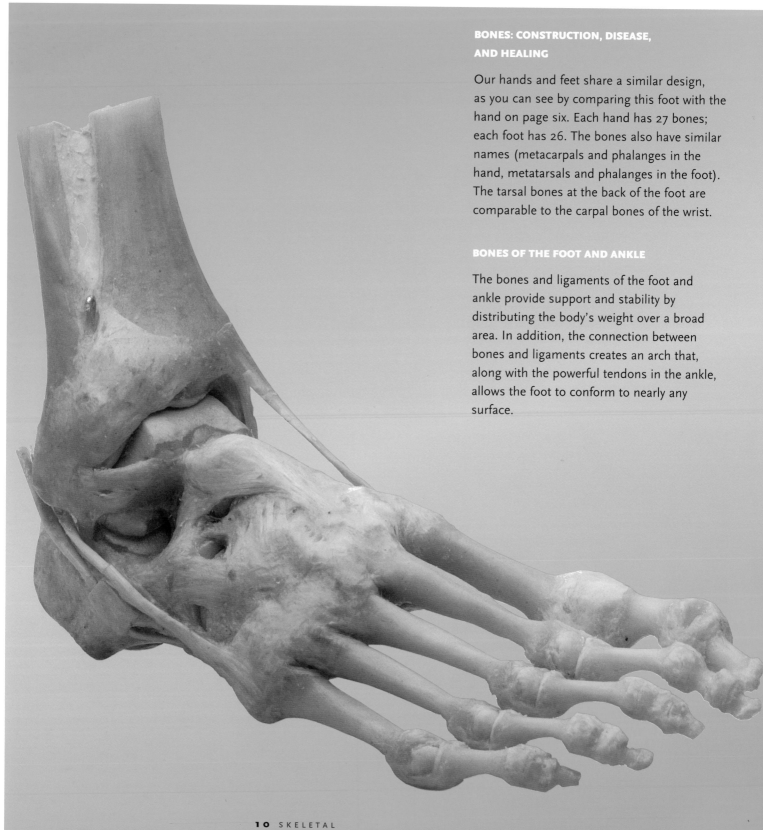

CORONAL SECTION OF FEMUR

The bones of the body are made of two types of tissue: spongy and compact. Spongy bone tissue, found at the ends of the long bones, like the femur (thighbone) shown above, makes bone lighter and distributes the force of impact. Compact bone tissue, which comprises the outer layer of long bones as well as the ribs and the skull, provides protection and support.

The shafts of long bones are hollow, containing a soft substance known as yellow marrow, an essential fat reserve. Red bone marrow is found in the ends of our long bones and manufactures most of our red blood cells, which carry oxygen throughout the body. In addition, the red marrow manufactures white blood cells that protect the body from invading bacteria and viruses.

HEALING BONE

When a bone fractures, bone cells rush to the scene and begin the healing process, which is similar to initial bone growth in fetal development. The tibia (shinbone), middle of page, was set incorrectly after its fracture, leading to distorted healing, known to affect the weight-bearing functions of the leg.

CANCEROUS BONE

Bone is constantly regenerating. Specialized bone cells create new bone, while other cells remove older bone. When bone cells grow out of control, cancer may occur. This humerus (arm bone, above right) developed a malignant cancer (osteogenic sarcoma) after suffering two fractures in three months. Cancer resulting from bone fracture is extremely rare.

OSTEOARTHRITIS

A chronic disease causing the deterioration of the joints, osteoarthritis most often affects the weight-bearing joints of the body, as well as the hands. The effects of osteoarthritis—swelling, pain, and loss of mobility—cannot be reversed. Symptoms can be relieved with anti-inflammatory medication, physical therapy, and weight loss. In some instances, as with the specimen here, osteoarthritis leads to a near-total breakdown of the cartilage in the joints of the fingers, exposing bone, and creating pain and deformity.

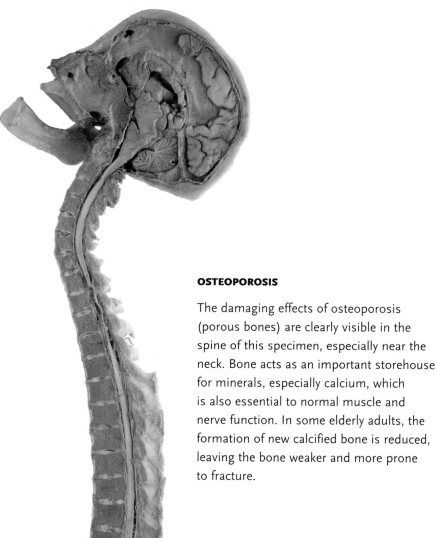

OSTEOPOROSIS

The damaging effects of osteoporosis (porous bones) are clearly visible in the spine of this specimen, especially near the neck. Bone acts as an important storehouse for minerals, especially calcium, which is also essential to normal muscle and nerve function. In some elderly adults, the formation of new calcified bone is reduced, leaving the bone weaker and more prone to fracture.

EXPANDED SKULL WITH TEMPORAL BONE AND AUDITORY OSSICLES

The convex shape and spongy middle layer of our cranial bones provide protection for the brain, absorbing and diffusing impact. The bones of the cranium are not tightly joined at birth, allowing them to overlap as the infant's skull passes through the birth canal. Known as soft spots, these bones grow together over the first two years of life, meeting at immovable joints called sutures.

Our skulls include the smallest bones in our bodies. Called auditory ossicles (hearing bones), they are located within the temporal bones of the skull and have distinct shapes for which they are named. They are the malleus (hammer), the incus (anvil), and the stapes (stirrup). Connected by the smallest moveable joints in the body, these bones transfer sound as vibrations from the larger eardrum to the smaller oval window of the inner ear.

Of the 22 bones in the adult skull, the only moveable bone is the mandible, or lower jaw.

TEMPORAL BONE

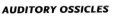

AUDITORY OSSICLES

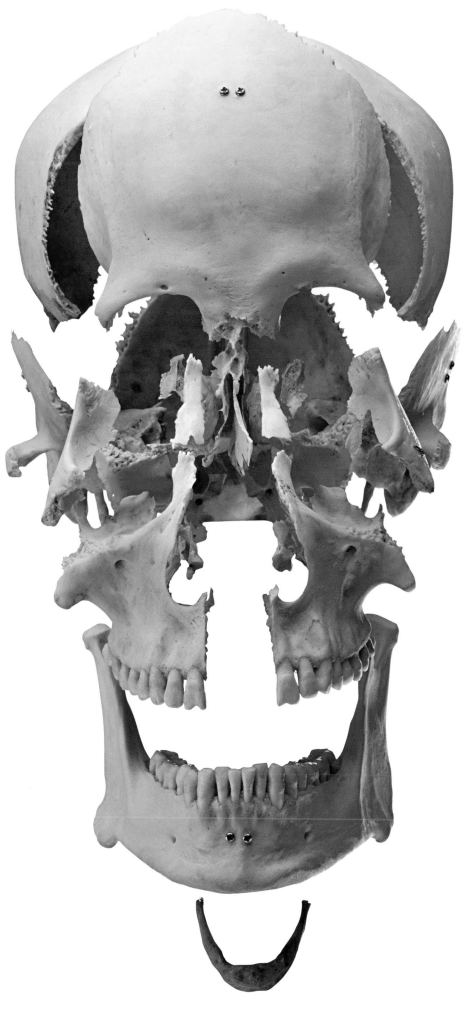

MUSCU
SYSTEM

SKELETAL MUSCLES

Skeletal muscles cover most of the body and account for much of our physical form. The body has more than 600 skeletal muscles that make up nearly half the weight of the human body. In addition, skeletal muscles provide:

Movement and posture Through contractions, muscles move our bodies. Muscle tone, a level of continual contraction, keeps us upright despite gravity.

Protection The internal organs of the abdominal cavity are protected and held in place by four muscle layers that connect at the rib cage and pelvic bones.

Body heat Through their contractions and cellular respiration, skeletal muscles play an important role in homeostasis, the mainte-nance of the body's constant temperature at 98.2°F (36.7°C). If the hypothalamus, the heat-promoting center in the brain, detects a drop in body temperature, it signals the muscles and we shiver. This increase in activity produces heat, thus raising the body's temperature.

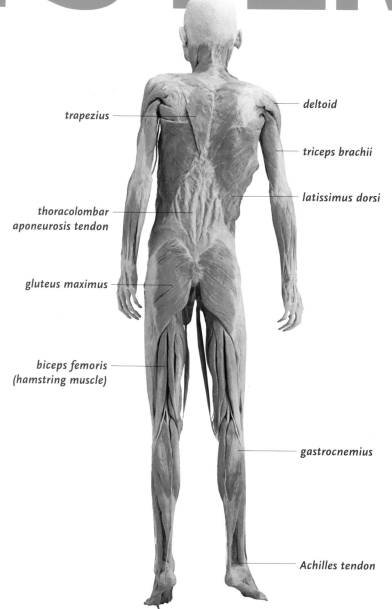

trapezius

deltoid

triceps brachii

latissimus dorsi

thoracolombar aponeurosis tendon

gluteus maximus

biceps femoris (hamstring muscle)

gastrocnemius

Achilles tendon

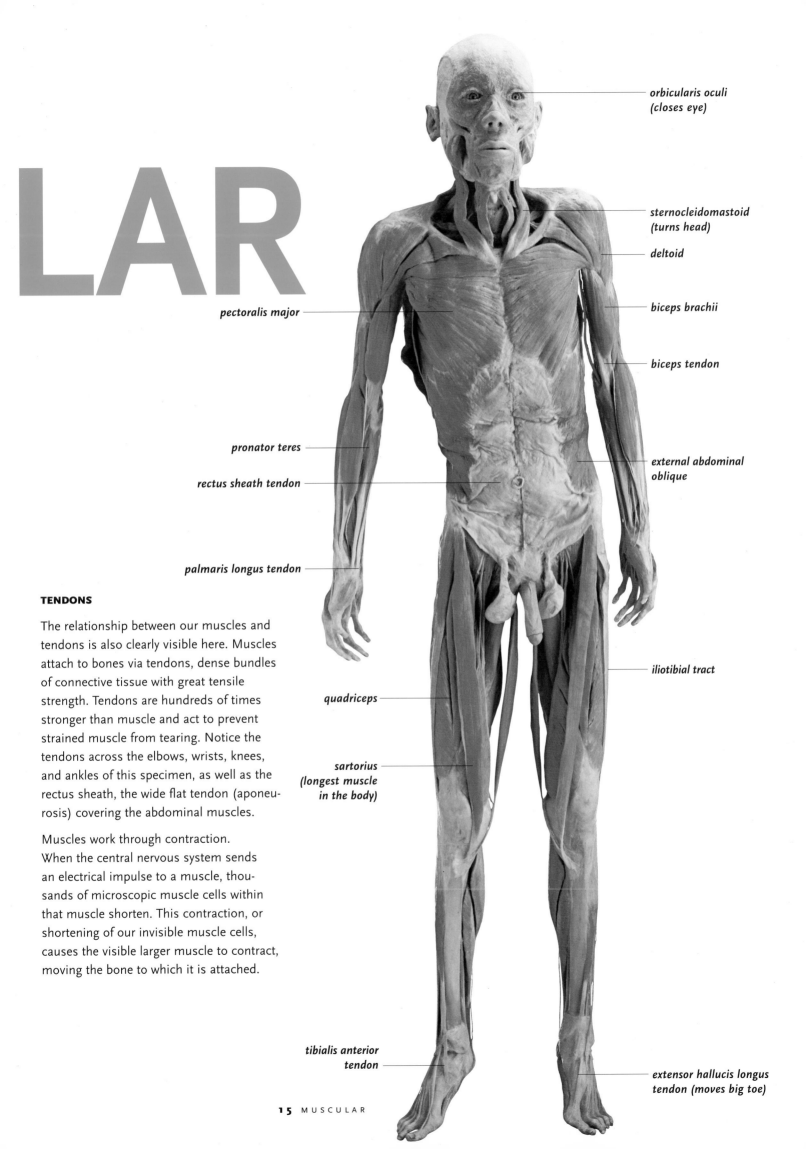

LAR

orbicularis oculi
(closes eye)

sternocleidomastoid
(turns head)

deltoid

biceps brachii

biceps tendon

external abdominal
oblique

iliotibial tract

pectoralis major

pronator teres

rectus sheath tendon

palmaris longus tendon

quadriceps

sartorius
(longest muscle
in the body)

tibialis anterior
tendon

extensor hallucis longus
tendon (moves big toe)

TENDONS

The relationship between our muscles and tendons is also clearly visible here. Muscles attach to bones via tendons, dense bundles of connective tissue with great tensile strength. Tendons are hundreds of times stronger than muscle and act to prevent strained muscle from tearing. Notice the tendons across the elbows, wrists, knees, and ankles of this specimen, as well as the rectus sheath, the wide flat tendon (aponeurosis) covering the abdominal muscles.

Muscles work through contraction. When the central nervous system sends an electrical impulse to a muscle, thousands of microscopic muscle cells within that muscle shorten. This contraction, or shortening of our invisible muscle cells, causes the visible larger muscle to contract, moving the bone to which it is attached.

This unique dissection allows you to see the relationship of the body's muscle layers and demonstrates the points at which these layers attach to the skeleton.

MUSCLE ATTACHMENT

Each muscle attaches to the skeleton at two points:

The *point of origin*, which lies closer to the centerline of the body and anchors the muscle to a fixed or immovable bone.

The *point of insertion*, which lies farther away from the centerline of the body and attaches the muscle to the less fixed or more moveable bone.

Between the muscle's point of origin and its point of insertion it crosses one or more joints. The contraction, or pull of the muscle at its point of insertion, results in movement of the bones to which it is attached at all of the joints it crosses.

In this dissection, every muscle has been separated from its point of origin and remains connected to its point of insertion.

MUSCLE LAYERING

This specimen also reveals every layer of skeletal muscle. Sometimes four layers deep, a stunning array of muscles work together for bodily support and movement. For example, the four layers of abdominal muscles cross the body in four different directions to firm and strengthen the abdominal wall. The muscles that run along the spine are some of the most powerful muscles of the body; they keep us upright and provide the strength forlifting and pushing.

As most muscles typically perform only one major function, every bodily movement requires several muscles working in concert to initiate and assist in a motion. For example, six muscles are required to move your eyeball, nine to move your arm, and sixteen to control the different facial expressions that allow us to express our emotions.

VOLUNTARY AND INVOLUNTARY MUSCLES

The body has voluntary and involuntary muscles. Voluntary muscles (striated) like the skeletal muscles discussed above, are under your control and can be moved at will. Squeezing your gluteus maximus muscles (buttocks) will give you an indication of the amount of control you have over a voluntary muscle.

The involuntary (smooth, cardiac) muscles work without any direction from you and perform vital functions in our respiratory, digestive, and cardiovascular systems, such as the beating of the heart and the movement of food through the digestive tract.

It has been suggested that if all the muscles in your body worked together, they would generate enough power to lift more than ten tons.

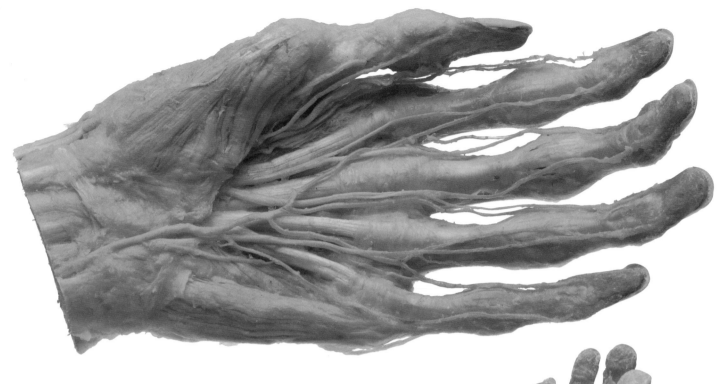

MUSCLES AND TENDONS
OF THE HANDS AND FEET

Our hands and feet contain a breathtaking
combination of muscles and tendons that
give us a tremendous range of mobility
and dexterity.

FLEXOR DIGITORUM SUPERFICIALIS TENDONS

The shiny cords (tendons) visible in the
palm of the specimen above are attached
to muscles in the forearm. They pull on
the fingers causing them to bend, allowing
us to grasp objects or to form a fist.

FLEXOR DIGITORUM LONGUS TENDONS

These tendons, the fanning shiny cords
visible at the center of this foot, permit
us to curl the very ends of our toes.

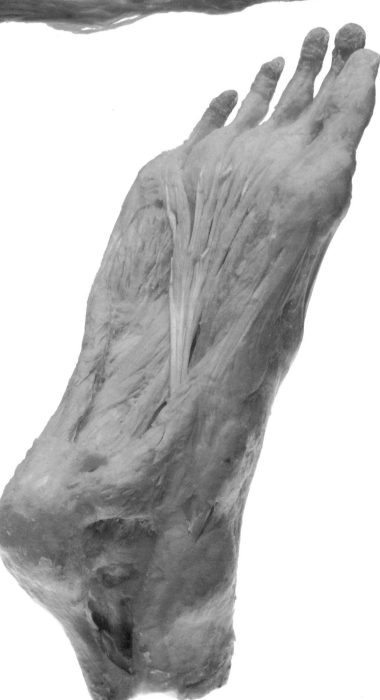

MUSCLE NAMES AND SHAPES

While muscle names often sound odd, they usually make a lot of sense. Muscles are most often named for their shape or location on the body, or for a combination of these factors.

DELTOID

The deltoid muscle, which joins the upper arm to the shoulder, was named for its shape, that of a triangle or *delta* in Greek.

BICEPS

The word "biceps" comes from two Latin words: *bi*, meaning two, and *cephalon*, meaning head. As you can clearly see from this specimen, one end of this muscle has two heads. The same principle applies to triceps (three heads) and quadriceps (four heads) muscles. Perhaps you didn't know that you have two biceps: one in the arm called the biceps brachii and one in the leg called the biceps femoris (hamstring) muscle.

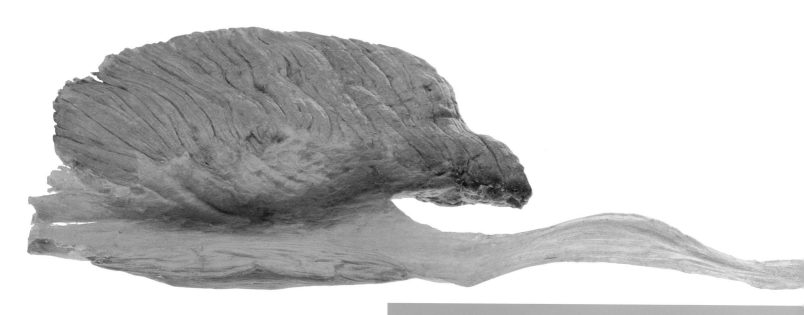

GLUTEUS MAXIMUS AND
ILIOTIBIAL TRACT

The gluteus maximus muscle is one of the
body's largest and strongest muscles. It is
used to extend and rotate your thigh when
walking and received its name from the
Greek word for "bottom." The three gluteal
muscles, minimus, medialus, and maximus,
are named according to their depth:
(minimus closest to the bone; maximus
closest to the surface). The long tendon
running across the top of the page is the
iliotibial tract that runs between the ilium
(hipbone) and the tibia (shinbone) on the
outside of your leg.

PECTORALIS MINOR

This dissection reveals the pectoralis minor,
the muscle that runs diagonally between the
chest and shoulder. It is one of five muscles
used when you reach out to give someone
an embrace. Because it is not the prime
mover, but only assists in this action,
it is known as a synergist muscle.

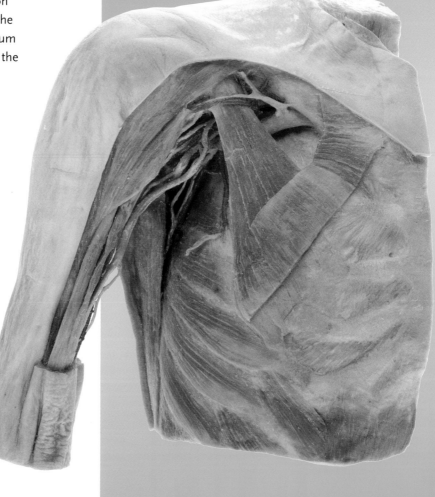

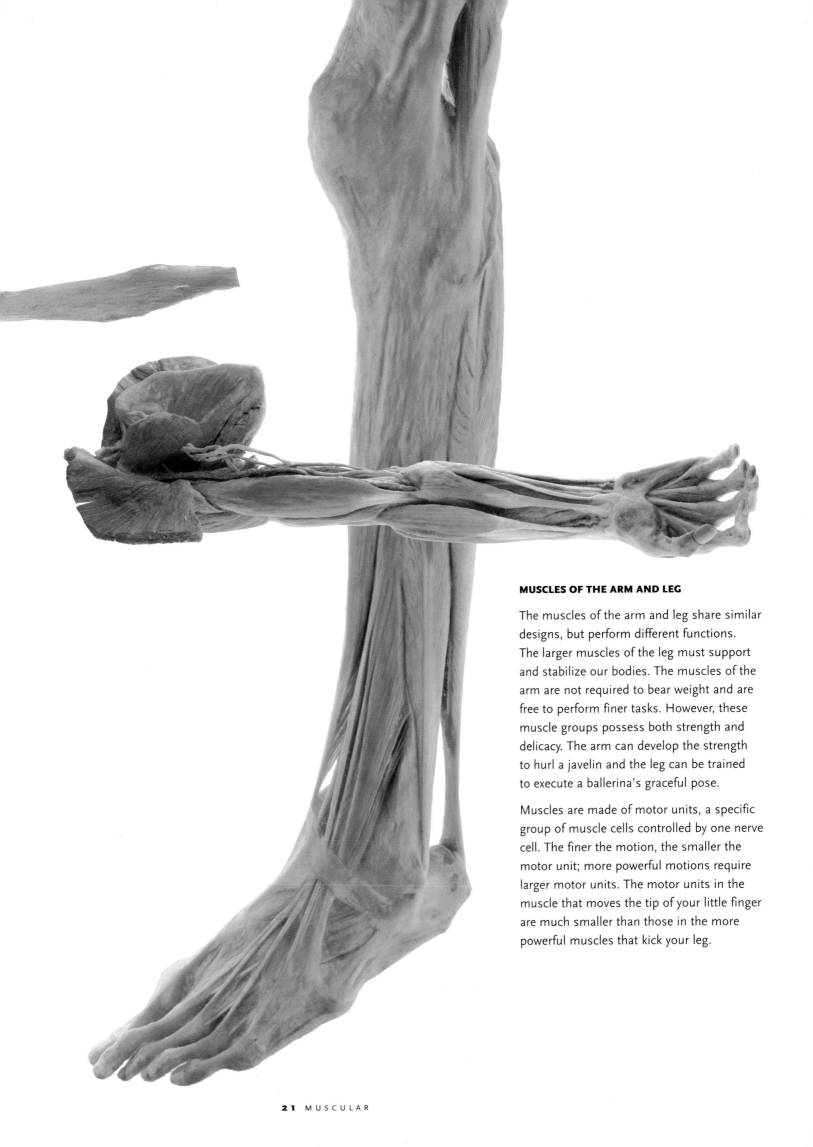

MUSCLES OF THE ARM AND LEG

The muscles of the arm and leg share similar designs, but perform different functions. The larger muscles of the leg must support and stabilize our bodies. The muscles of the arm are not required to bear weight and are free to perform finer tasks. However, these muscle groups possess both strength and delicacy. The arm can develop the strength to hurl a javelin and the leg can be trained to execute a ballerina's graceful pose.

Muscles are made of motor units, a specific group of muscle cells controlled by one nerve cell. The finer the motion, the smaller the motor unit; more powerful motions require larger motor units. The motor units in the muscle that moves the tip of your little finger are much smaller than those in the more powerful muscles that kick your leg.

NERVOUS

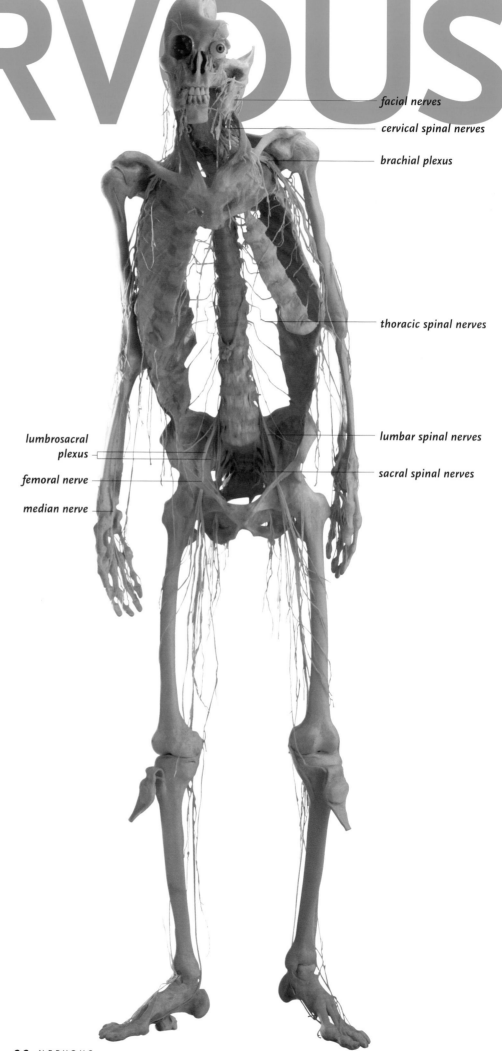

facial nerves

cervical spinal nerves

brachial plexus

thoracic spinal nerves

lumbrosacral plexus

femoral nerve

median nerve

lumbar spinal nerves

sacral spinal nerves

CENTRAL AND PERIPHERAL NERVOUS SYSTEM

The brain and spinal cord make up the central nervous system. All other nerves, which branch from the brain and spinal cord into finer and finer divisions to the very edges of the body, comprise the peripheral nervous system. The peripheral nervous system continually updates the central nervous system, sending information via sensory nerves to the brain, where more than one trillion nerve cells process that information. Once brain cells have determined the appropriate response to a stimulus, they send commands back to the body through motor nerves. The main features visible on this specimen include:

Cranial nerves Twelve nerves that originate in the brain stem and control the muscles of the face and eyes, and transmit sight, sound, and taste to the brain.

Spinal nerves Thirty-two pairs of nerves that stem from the spinal cord. The spinal nerves are named for the region of the spine from which they emerge: cervical, thoracic, lumbar, and sacral. They branch out from between each of our vertebrae, allowing the spinal cord to connect with the skeletal muscles of the trunk and limbs.

Nerve plexi The nerve plexi, located under the arms and on the inner surface of the pelvis of this specimen, are dense networks in which nerves combine to send and receive information to and from the upper and lower limbs. The plexi under each arm are called the brachial plexi; those on the inner surface of the pelvis and sacrum are called the lumbar, and sacral plexi.

Femoral nerves Emerging from the lumbar plexus, the femoral nerves send and receive information to and from the thigh, leg, ankle, and foot.

SYSTEM

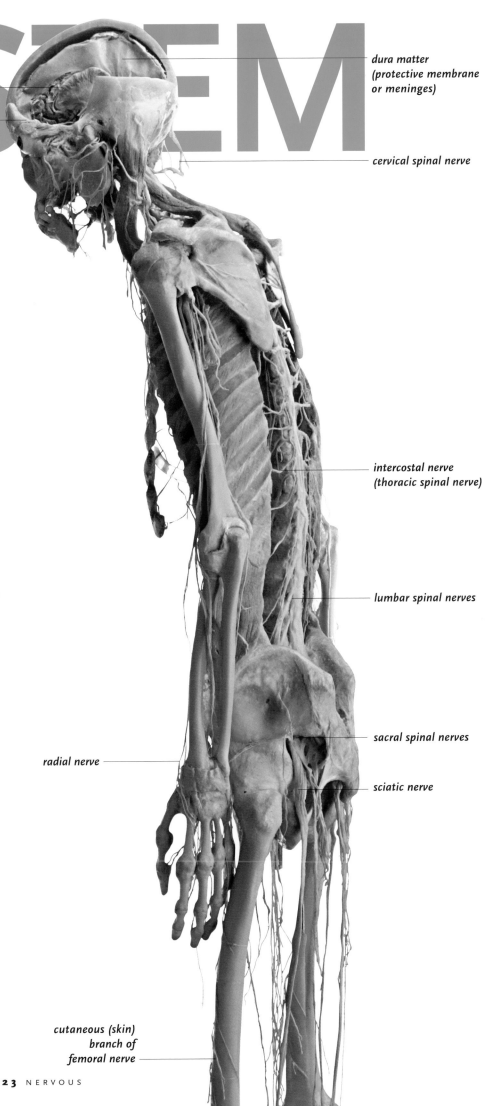

internal capsule

lacrimal gland
(tear gland)

dura matter
(protective membrane
or meninges)

cervical spinal nerve

intercostal nerve
(thoracic spinal nerve)

lumbar spinal nerves

radial nerve

sacral spinal nerves

sciatic nerve

cutaneous (skin)
branch of
femoral nerve

INTERNAL CAPSULE AND
PERIPHERAL NERVES

All information traveling to or from our
brains first passes through the brain's
internal capsule, the shell-like disc visible
deep within the left side of this specimen's
skull. The internal capsule receives
information and routes it in every direction
necessary. The ascending fibers allow us
to consciously process sensory information,
while the descending fibers allow us to
voluntarily contract our skeletal muscles.

Most of the peripheral nerves are visible
on this specimen. These include the nerves
of the autonomic (involuntary) nervous
system, which control essential bodily
functions such as heartbeat, breathing,
and digestion.

Autonomic nerves also regulate the body's
fight or flight response when danger is
perceived. That is when the heart speeds up,
the sweat glands kick in, the liver pumps
glucose into the bloodstream for energy,
and the brain becomes hyper-alert.
In addition, the blood flow is diverted
from the skin to the organs, producing
that cold, clammy feeling.

The largest nerve in the body, the sciatic
nerve, is also visible on this dissection.
Beginning at the buttocks, it innervates
(supplies) nerve impulses to the back of
the thigh and the muscle below the knee.
Increased pressure on this nerve causes
sciatica, resulting in extreme pain that
runs down the back of the thigh and leg.

NERVES OF THE HAND

The nerves of the hand are part of the peripheral nervous system and include motor nerves and sensory nerves. Motor nerves, which carry impulses from the brain to the body, command the fingers and thumb to move. Sensory nerves, which transmit information about the body and the outside environment to the brain, detect everything from the stretch of muscles and joints, to pressure in the blood vessels.

As the main conduit between the brain and the body, the spinal cord transmits millions of nerve impulses per seconds at speeds exceeding 270 miles (434 kilometers) per hour.

Your spinal cord is approximately 17 inches (43 centimeters) and stops growing when you are about five years old. Because you and your spinal bones continue to grow, the spinal cord does not extend the entire length of your spine. In fact, it stops several vertebrae above the hips. With the meninges (the connective tissue layers that surround the spinal cord) removed from the base of the spinal cord on this specimen, you can see that the spinal cord branches into dozens of fine nerves. This region, known as the cauda equina, or "horse's tail," continues to the base of the spine where connective tissue attaches it to the coccyx (tailbone), holding the cord in place.

Signals from sensory nerves all over the body travel up the spinal cord (only the width of a finger) to the brain where we become aware of them. In some cases, the body reacts before a sensory impulse reaches the brain. Think of the involuntary reaction you have when you pull your hand away from something hot. This response is known as a reflex. As soon as the spinal cord receives a distressed nerve impulse, it commands the endangered part of the body to move.

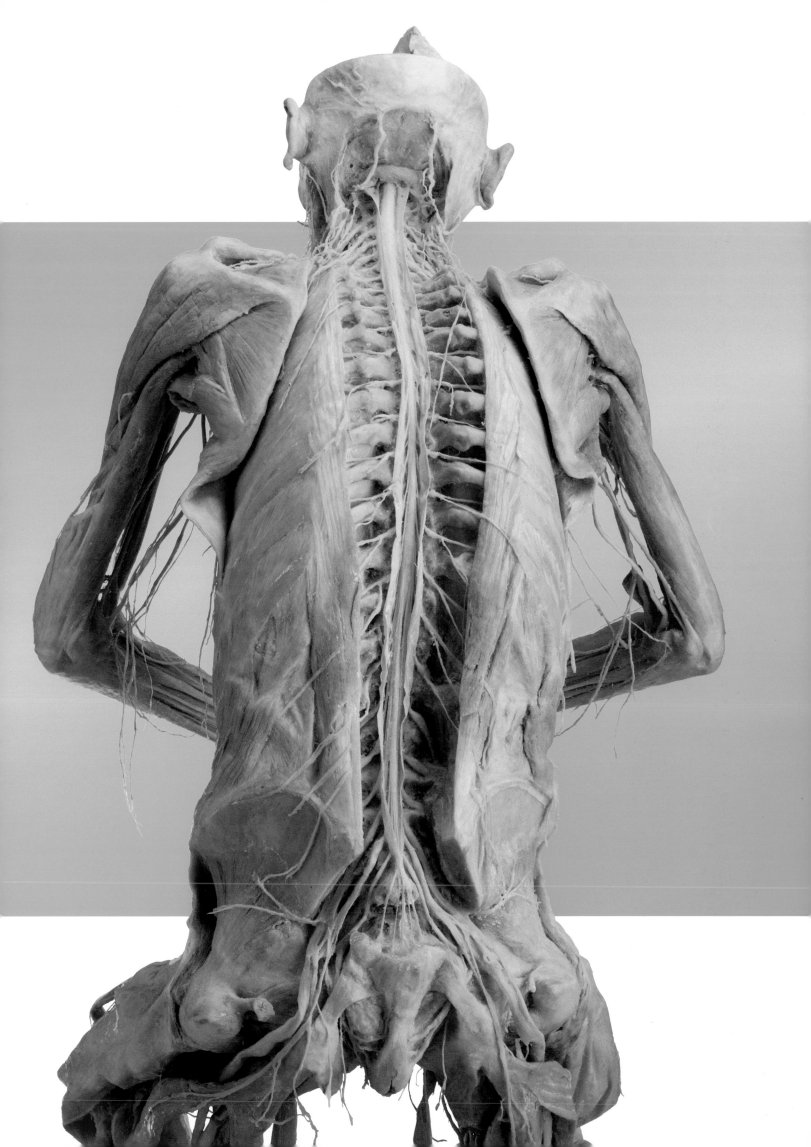

NERVE PATHWAYS

Several of the cranial nerves deep in the brain, which activate the muscles and organs of the face, are visible in the right side of this specimen's face. These include:

The trigeminal nerves This web of nerves controls muscles of chewing and of the teeth. They are also the nerves most affected by migraine headaches.

The optic nerve Visible deep within the right eye of this specimen, it transmits images from the eye to the sight centers in the brain.

This dissection also illustrates the "Van principle," which states that the large nerves of the body are usually accompanied by similarly named arteries and veins. For example, the femoral nerve, the femoral artery, and the femoral vein (not shown here) follow the same course into the upper thigh.

Major arteries on this specimen include:

The aorta The main artery of the circulatory system, it transports blood to all parts of the body.

The common, external, and internal iliac arteries Beginning in the abdomen where the aorta branches, they deliver blood to the pelvic region and lower limbs.

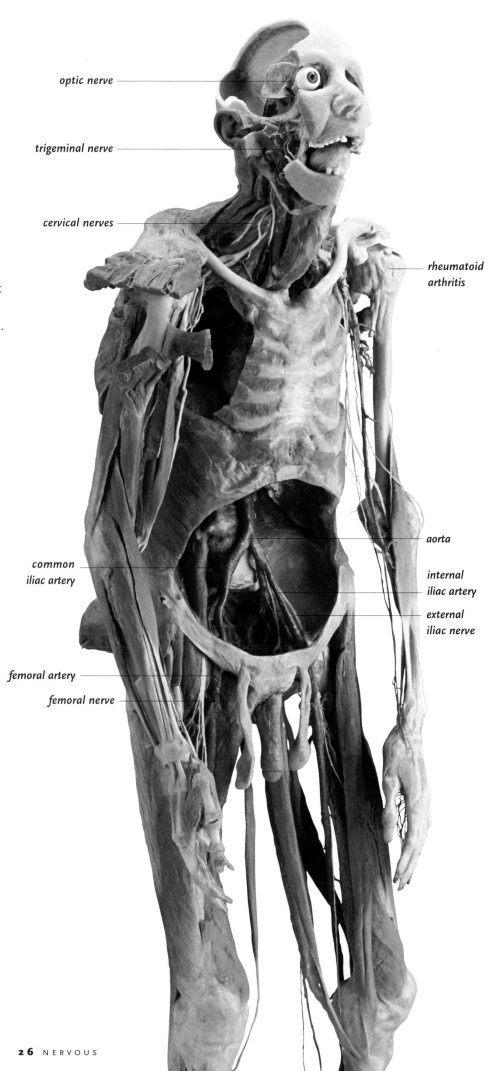

optic nerve

trigeminal nerve

cervical nerves

rheumatoid arthritis

aorta

internal iliac artery

external iliac nerve

common iliac artery

femoral artery

femoral nerve

CARPAL TUNNEL

The right wrist of this specimen clearly demonstrates the carpal tunnel, the site of the aliment known as carpal tunnel syndrome, a common malady today with our repetitive use of computers. This syndrome occurs when tendons become inflamed and press on the median nerve within the carpal tunnel, a space located immediately above the carpal bones in the wrist.

RHEUMATOID ARTHRITIS

This specimen also shows signs of rheumatoid arthritis in the left shoulder. The pitting in the bone results from this autoimmune disease, in which the body's own defenses begin to attack the cartilage, breaking it down. Symptoms also include joint swelling, pain, and stiffness, as well as muscle weakness, osteoporosis, and associated heart and blood vessel problems.

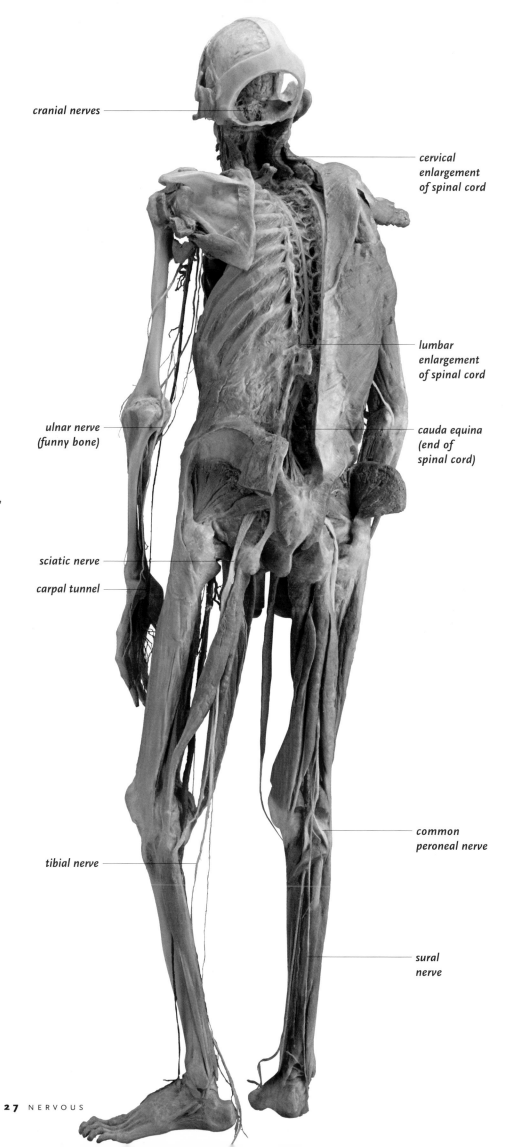

cranial nerves

cervical enlargement of spinal cord

lumbar enlargement of spinal cord

ulnar nerve (funny bone)

cauda equina (end of spinal cord)

sciatic nerve

carpal tunnel

common peroneal nerve

tibial nerve

sural nerve

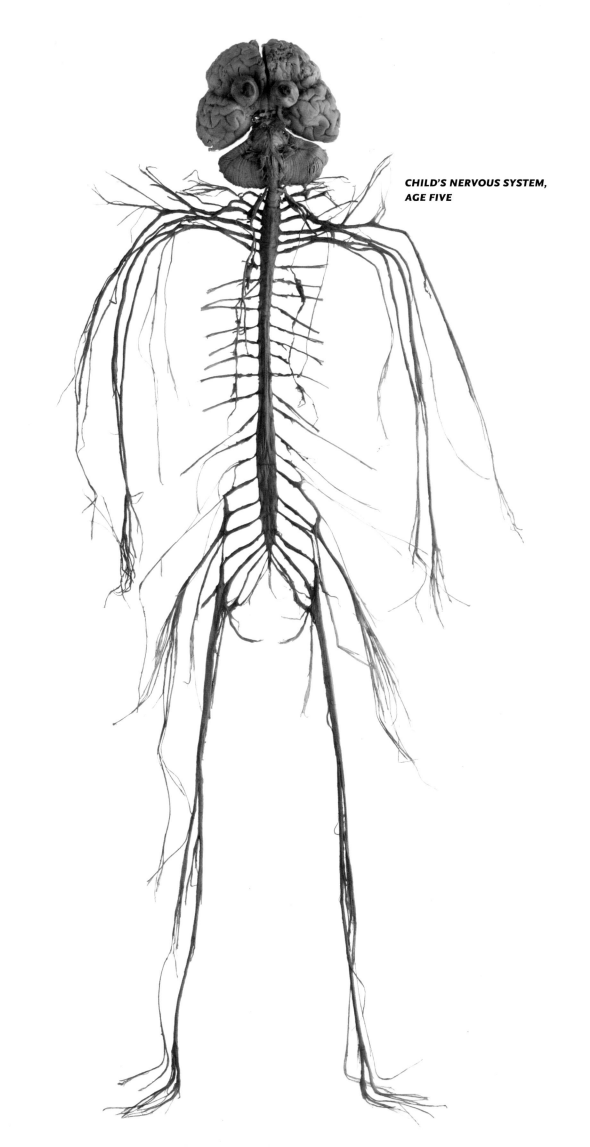

CHILD'S NERVOUS SYSTEM,
AGE FIVE

THE BRAIN

The brain is the mysterious central organ of the nervous system. It is essential for all bodily functions and contains at least a trillion nerve cells, which are in constant communication with each other and the body. Some brain cells make connections with over 10,000 others in a split second.

The largest parts of the brain, the two cerebral hemispheres, are covered by a layer of gray matter called the cerebral cortex. This is the seat of all higher brain functions, including, memory, thought, behavior, and personality. Humans are the only animals who know that they are thinking.

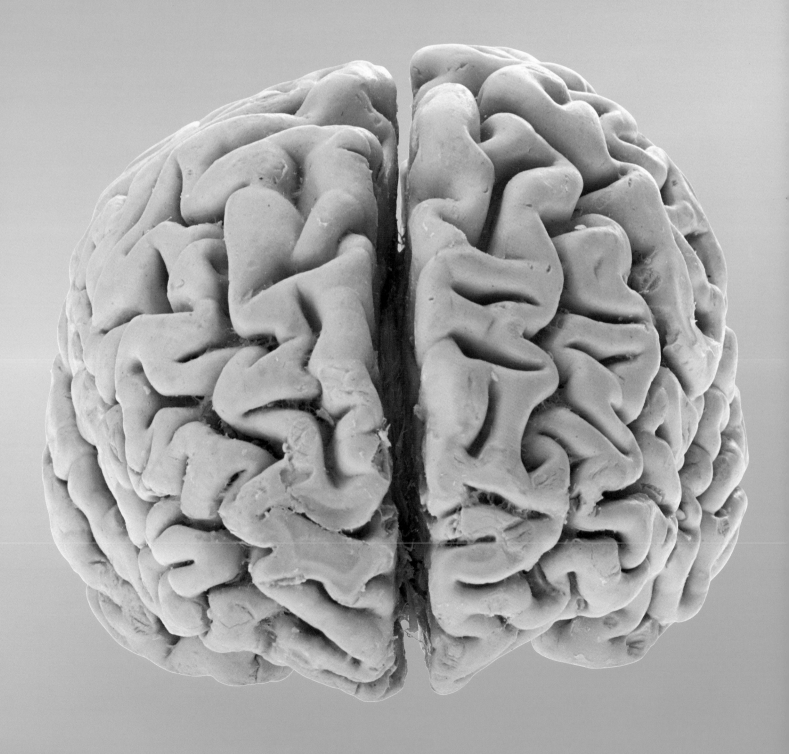

BRAIN SECTION WITH VENTRICLES

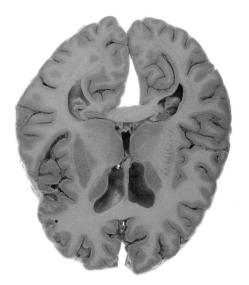

CEREBRAL VENTRICLES AND CEREBROSPINAL FLUID

Inside the brain are hollow spaces called ventricles. They are filled with a clear water-like fluid called the cerebrospinal fluid. Made within the ventricles, this fluid also circulates between the meninges (the protective membrane that surrounds the brain and spinal cord), cushioning the brain and keeping it clean. The cerebrospinal fluid is continuously reabsorbed and completely regenerated every six hours. If a blockage prevents the cerebrospinal fluid from circulating, a condition known as hydrocephalus (water on the brain) may result, leading to swelling of the brain ventricles

BRAIN WITH MASSIVE HEMORRHAGE

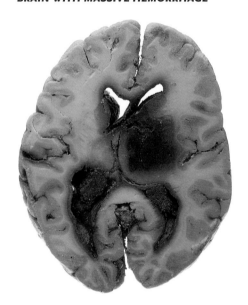

STROKE

Although it weights only 3 pounds (1.4 kilograms) on average, the brain requires over 20 percent of our body's total blood supply. If this blood supply is interrupted for even a brief period of time, brain tissues will die.

This is the case with stroke. It is caused by a blockage or rupture in one or more of the brain's blood vessels. A broken vessel fills part of the brain with blood, increasing pressure and leading to further tissue death. Those with high blood pressure and arteriosclerosis are at greater risk for this to occur. Symptoms of stroke include paralyses, and language, sensory, and vision impairment.

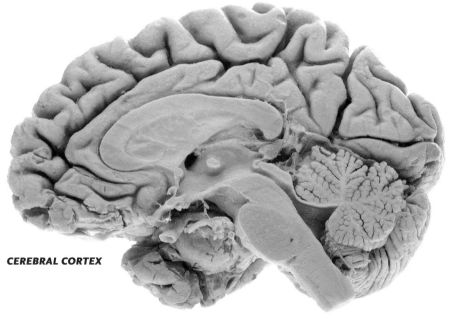

CEREBRAL CORTEX

GYRUS AND GRAY MATTER

Due to its rapid growth through evolution, the cerebral cortex, has developed folds to fit into the skull. This gives the brain its wrinkled appearance. Each fold is called a gyrus. Human brains are broadly similar in appearance, though a few gyri can vary according to the individual. The gray matter on the surface of each gyrus is comprised of neurons (brain cells). Beneath the gray matter is white matter, which transmits information, such as muscle movement and speech, between the cortex and other parts of the body. If spread out, the cortex would cover more than three square feet (one square meter).

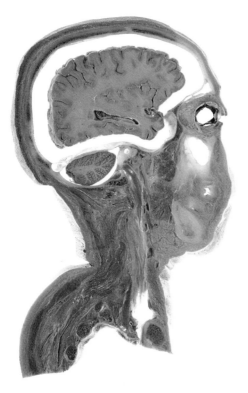
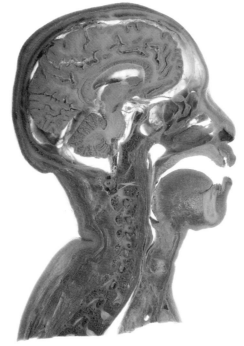
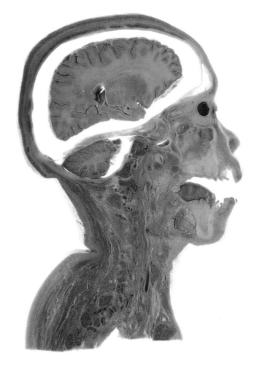

THE SPECIAL SENSES

SIGHT

Think of your eye as a camera with its lens inside. Light reflected from an image passes through the pupil (the black spot in the middle of your eye) to the lens just behind. The lens focuses that light to hit the retina, which is light sensitive and turns the image into nerve impulses. The optic nerve then collects these impulses from the retina and transmits them to the sight center of the brain, where pictures are developed.

SMELL

When inhaling air through the nostrils, the chemicals in the air bind with the microscopic hairs at the top of the nasal cavity. This bond creates a nerve impulse that travels through the olfactory nerve fibers to the olfactory center in the cerebral cortex, where it registers as a smell. You have between 10 and 20 million olfactory receptors in your nose that are capable of responding to as many as 4,000 different odors. On average, women are more sensitive to odors than men.

TASTE

Taste buds lie in the grooves between the bumps in your tongue and contain chemical receptor cells for specific tastes. At the tip of the tongue, taste buds are most sensitive to sweets. Along the sides of the tongue, the buds are most sensitive to salty and sour tastes. At the back of the tongue, the chemical receptors react to the bitter in our diets.

When tiny fibers within the taste buds bind with molecules of food, they send an impulse to the brain. The brain uses this taste information to determine the type of food you are eating.

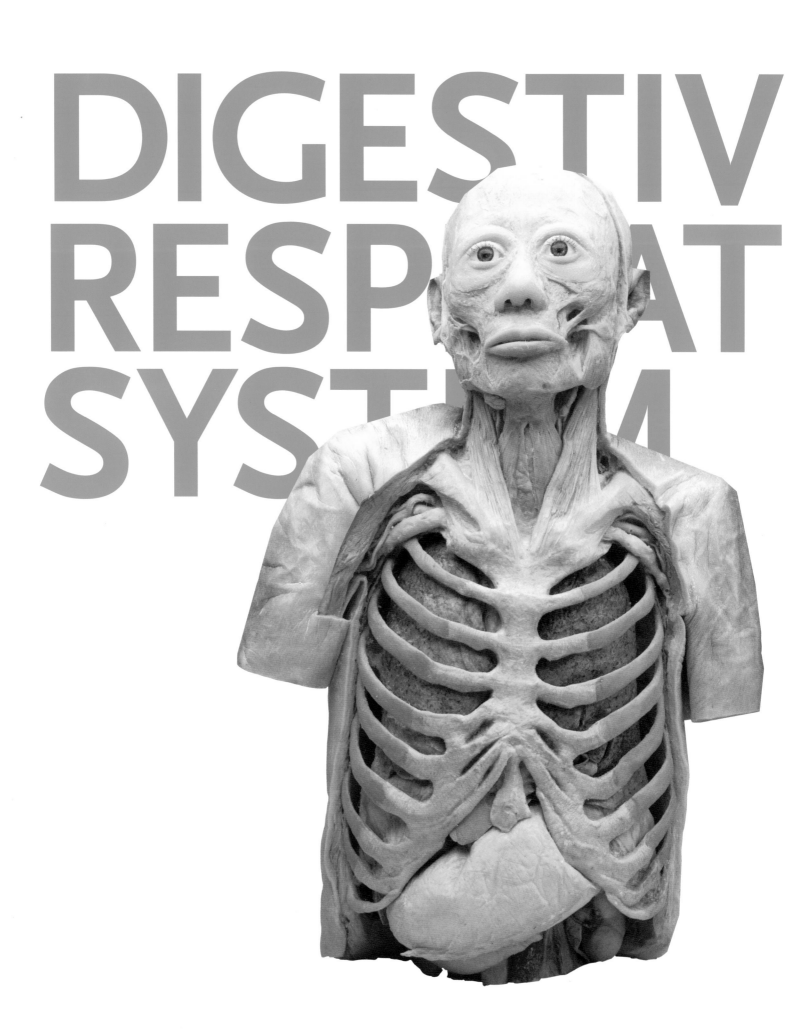

DIGESTIV
RESPI AT
SYSTE

E+ ORY

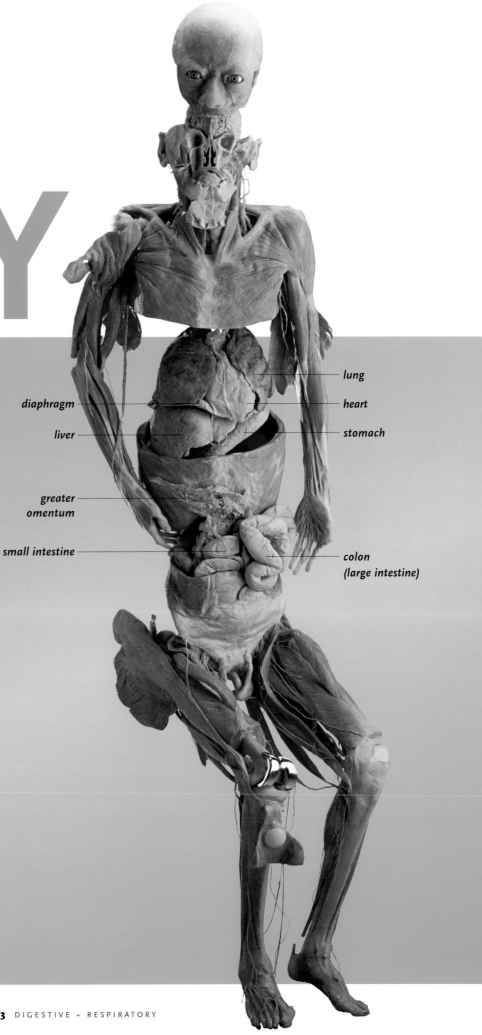

ORGANS OF THE THORAX AND ABDOMEN

This vertical dissection provides a rare view into the compact and complex relationship of the body's organs. The main organs of the thorax, or chest cavity, are the lungs and heart. Here, oxygen is extracted from the outside air and circulated into the bloodstream where it is transported to every cell in the body. The heart's placement between the lungs makes clear its central role in respiration and circulation.

The abdominal cavity, below the lungs, contains the six organs of the digestive system. Approximately 25 feet long (7.6 meters), our digestive system fits within the relatively small confines of our abdomens. No space is wasted: the liver and pancreas fit neatly under the lungs and diaphragm, and the gallbladder tucks behind the liver. The stomach also partly lodges behind the liver, while the small intestine coils upon itself within the large intestine.

The greater omentum secures the stomach and part of the small intestines to the body wall, supplying them with nerves and blood vessels. A connective tissue, the omentum is one of the areas where the body stores fat, and it also helps defend the digestive organs against infection. On this specimen it has been folded back to expose the intestines.

diaphragm

liver

greater omentum

small intestine

lung

heart

stomach

colon (large intestine)

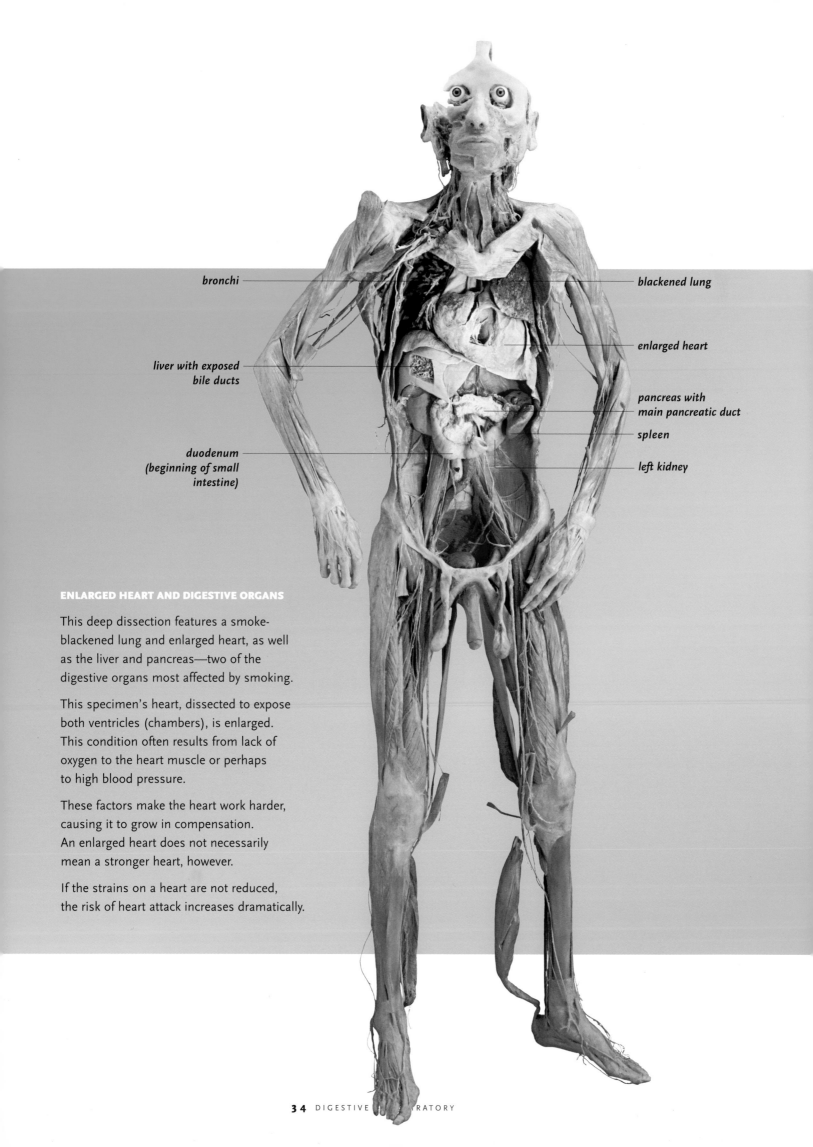

bronchi

blackened lung

enlarged heart

liver with exposed
bile ducts

pancreas with
main pancreatic duct

spleen

duodenum
(beginning of small
intestine)

left kidney

ENLARGED HEART AND DIGESTIVE ORGANS

This deep dissection features a smoke-blackened lung and enlarged heart, as well as the liver and pancreas—two of the digestive organs most affected by smoking.

This specimen's heart, dissected to expose both ventricles (chambers), is enlarged. This condition often results from lack of oxygen to the heart muscle or perhaps to high blood pressure.

These factors make the heart work harder, causing it to grow in compensation. An enlarged heart does not necessarily mean a stronger heart, however.

If the strains on a heart are not reduced, the risk of heart attack increases dramatically.

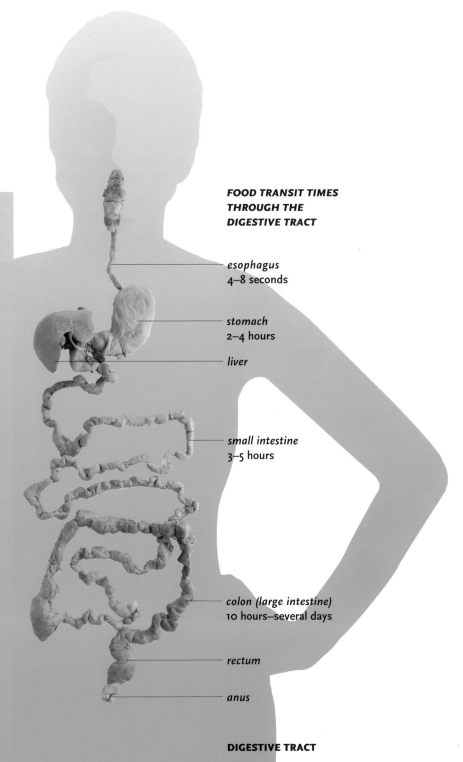

LIVER AND PANCREAS

The liver and pancreas create the enzymes that help digest our food.

The pancreas also produces insulin, which helps regulate the level of glucose in our blood. Glucose, a type of simple sugar, is the main energy source for our cells. When pancreatic cells cannot produce enough insulin and glucose levels in the body rise, the disease diabetes may occur.

The dissection of the pancreas on this specimen exposes the main pancreatic duct through which our digestive enzymes reach the duodenum, the first part of the small intestine. This liver's dissection reveals some of the millions of small passageways through which bile, secreted by the liver, is transported to the gallbladder for storage or directly to the duodenum where it works to breakdown fats. Because smoking restricts oxygen to the body and alters blood sugar levels, a smoker's liver and pancreas must work harder, with less oxygen, to maintain balance in the body. This can lead to stress and tissue death.

SPLEEN

The spleen is also visible on the left side of this specimen. An organ whose major function is to filter blood, the spleen is not essential for life; it may be removed if badly damaged.

FOOD TRANSIT TIMES THROUGH THE DIGESTIVE TRACT

esophagus
4–8 seconds

stomach
2–4 hours

liver

small intestine
3–5 hours

colon (large intestine)
10 hours–several days

rectum

anus

DIGESTIVE TRACT

A fibro-muscular tube that runs from mouth to anus, the digestive tract and its accessory organs convert what we eat and drink into the nutrients we need to function.

TONGUE, PHARYNX, AND ESOPHAGUS

Digestion of food begins in the mouth with the teeth and tongue. The teeth tear, bite, and grind food, mixing it with saliva. The tongue moves food between the teeth to assist in chewing and swallowing. When food is swallowed, the epiglottis, a cartilaginous flap in the throat, closes the airway to prevent choking. Food then enters the esophagus where it is transported to the stomach in part by peristalsis (muscular contraction), which occurs throughout the digestive tract.

RUGAE

The stomach contains many rugae (folds), which disappear as the stomach fills with food to create more surface area. Cells within the rugae produce both mucus and digestive juices. We feel full from eating when nerve receptors in the stomach tell the brain that the stomach has stretched far enough.

STOMACH

In the stomach, three layers of muscle churn partially digested food with powerful gastric juices, turning the food into a paste-like substance called chyme, and killing many bacteria that might otherwise bring disease to the body. Our stomachs vary greatly in size and shape, depending upon eating habits and diet.

SECTION OF SMALL INTESTINE

The small intestine performs most of the digestion and absorption of nutrients in the digestive tract. It contains several million villi and microvilli, microscopic, finger-like projections that reach into the hollow spaces of the intestine increasing the small intestine's surface area over a thousand times. Through these projections, digested molecules pass into the bloodstream and are carried to the liver for further processing.

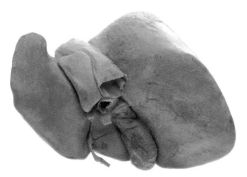

LIVER

The heaviest single organ in the body, weighing close to 3.5 pounds (1.6 kilograms) in an adult, the liver serves several metabolic functions. It produces bile, key to the proper digestion of fats; it stores vitamin A; and it produces several proteins essential to blood flow and clotting. The liver also receives glucose-rich blood returning from the digestive tract and converts much of this glucose into glycogen, which your body cells store as reserve energy.

CIRRHOTIC LIVER

Along with storing sugar, the liver also removes and destroys ingested toxins, including alcohol, drugs, and microbes. The improper diet that often accompanies alcohol and drug abuse can lead to the death of liver cells and their replacement by scar tissue. This disease is known as cirrhosis and is visible on this specimen. Other diseases, such as liver cancer and hepatitis, can also severely damage the liver.

LIVER BLOOD SUPPLY AND GALLBLADDER

This special dissection reveals the inner workings of the liver, including the pathways that blood takes through the organ. Two types of blood enter the liver: oxygen-rich from the heart (red cells) and nutrient-rich from the intestines (white cells). As blood passes through the liver, it is either cleansed or fortified. Bile, essential for the proper digestion of fats, flows from the liver in separate ducts and is stored in the gallbladder (yellow pouch) until needed for digestion.

THE SKELETAL AND MUSCULAR SYSTEMS WITH SMOKER'S LUNG

As an overview, this specimen provides an insight into the muscular and skeletal systems. In addition, it has been further dissected to reveal a blackened left lung.

The tars in tobacco permeate lung tissue, including the alveoli at the ends of the airways where the oxygen passes into the blood stream. The membranes between the alveoli and the bloodstream are only one micrometer thick. Smoking debris deposited in this membrane causes it to breakdown, thus decreasing the surface area in the lung and making breathing more difficult.

A healthy pair of lungs contains more than 300 million alveoli whose total surface area would cover half a football field. This smoker most likely had only half of that surface area with which to breathe.

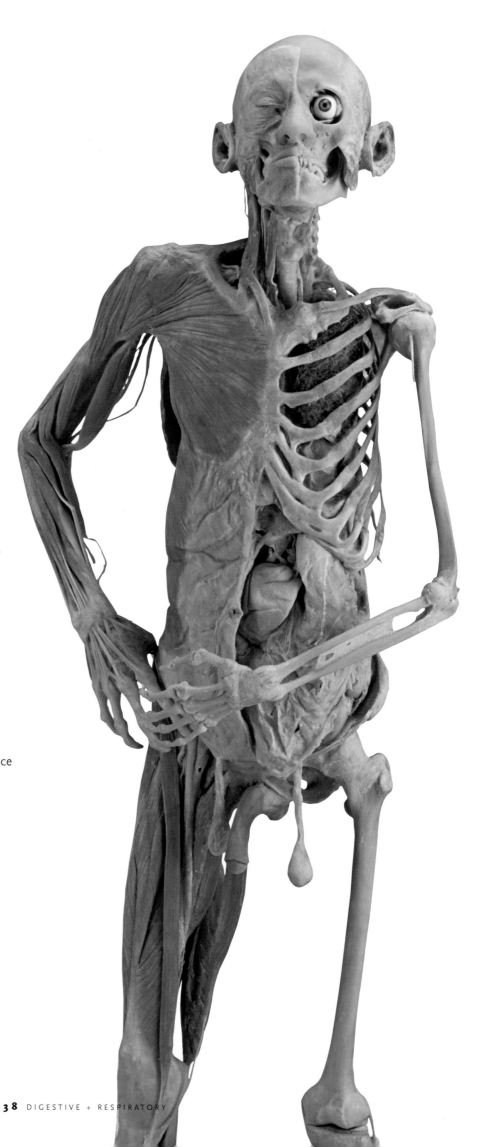

CEREBRAL CORTEX

A section of this specimen's skull has been removed to reveal the brain. This is a particularly good example of the way our brains fold to fit into the skull, compressing more than 3 square feet (2.8 square meters) of white and gray matter into a space less than one foot (.09 square meters) in diameter.

SCOLIOSIS

In addition to a smoking related illness, this specimen also exhibits mild scoliosis of the spine near the base of its neck. An abnormal curvature of the spine, scoliosis is caused by both genetic and environmental factors. It can lead to back and neck pain, as well as to severe deformity if not detected and corrected at an early age. Treatments to correct scoliosis include exercise, metal braces, and, in some cases, surgical intervention.

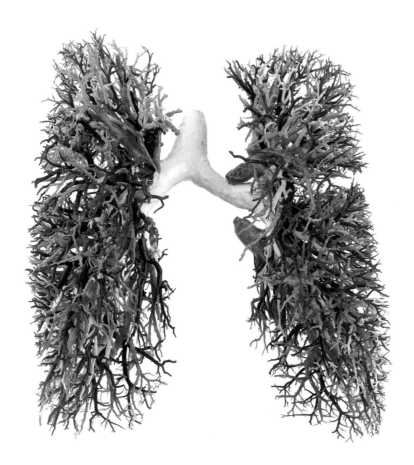

BRONCHIAL TREE

This dissection of a bronchial tree shows the close relationship between the arteries, veins, and airways in the lungs where gas exchange occurs. Also know as external respiration, gas exchange is the process in the lungs by which the blood releases carbon dioxide and absorbs oxygen, carrying it to every cell in the body.

The arteries in our lungs (blue on this specimen) carry carbon dioxide-rich blood from the heart to the edges of the bronchial tree or alveoli, (white on this specimen). When the alveoli are filled with oxygen-rich air, gas exchange occurs. Oxygenated blood then travels back to the heart through veins (red on this specimen) for circulation throughout the body. In most of the body, arteries carry oxygen and veins carry more carbon dioxide. In the lungs, however, this is reversed.

LUNG SECTION WITH CANCER AND EMPHYSEMA

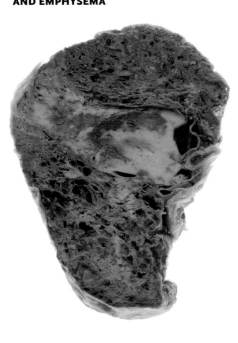

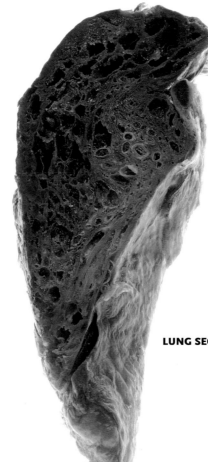

LUNG SECTION WITH EMPHYSEMA

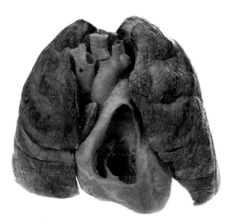

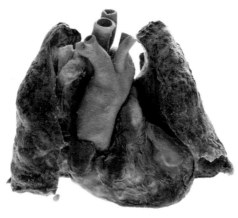

HEALTHY LUNGS AND HEART

DISEASED LUNGS WITH HEART ATTACK

These shrunken and darkened lungs illustrate the tar build-up and disease that often accompanies cigarette smoking. Visible is the close relationship between the lungs and heart (center of specimen), which together are responsible for circulating oxygenated blood through the body. Damage or disease to the lungs may lead to a heart attack, visible here as black streaks crossing the heart.

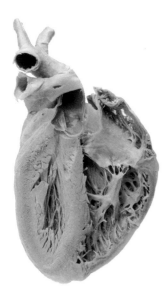

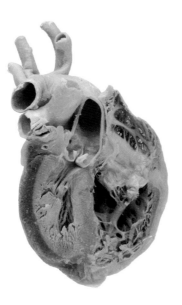

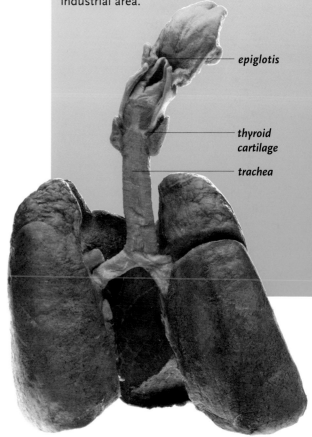

— *epiglotis*

— *thyroid cartilage*

— *trachea*

HEALTHY HEART

INFARCT HEART

This heart suffered infarct (tissue death) following a massive heart attack. The dead tissue appears as a thick black streak along the muscle of the left ventricle.

REPRODU
URINARY
SYSTEM

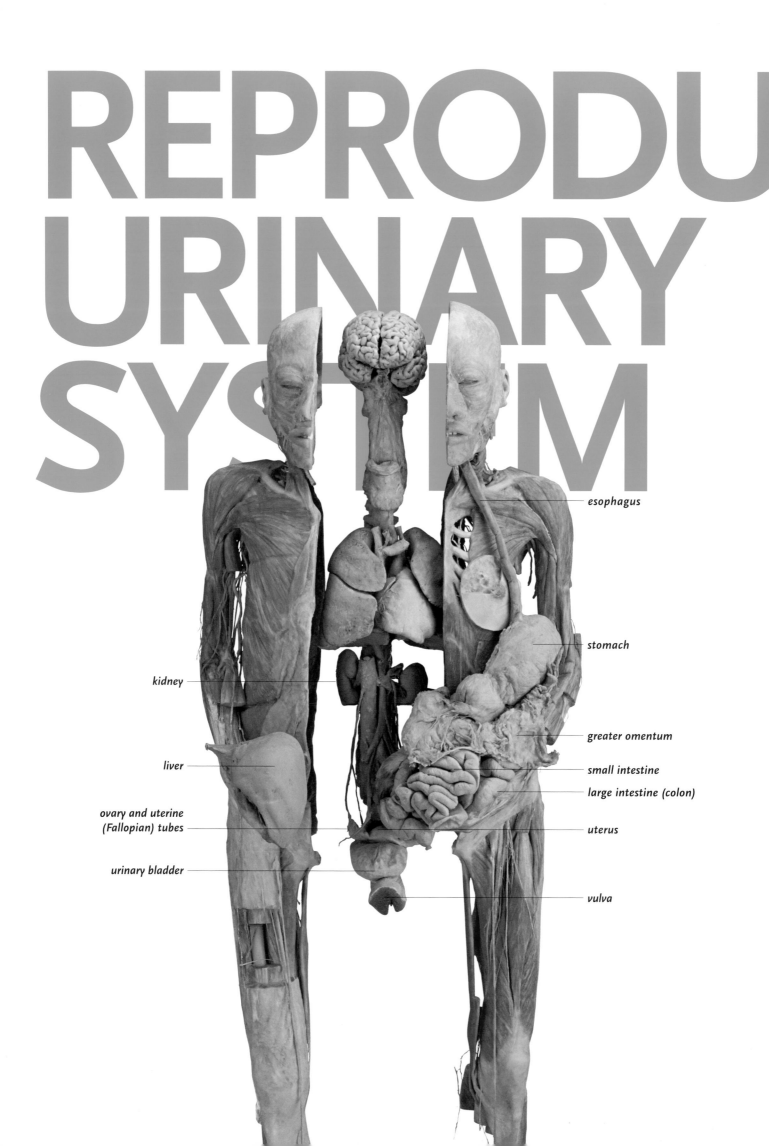

esophagus

stomach

kidney

greater omentum

liver

small intestine

large intestine (colon)

ovary and uterine
(Fallopian) tubes

uterus

urinary bladder

vulva

CTIVE+

FEMALE REPRODUCTIVE SYSTEM

Moving the abdominal viscera to one side, this dissection exposes the organs of the female reproductive system. Located behind the juncture of the pubic bones, the female reproductive system includes:

Ovaries They contain the ova (eggs) or female sex cells.

Fallopian tubes They transport the egg from the ovary to the uterus.

Uterus (womb) Embryonic and fetal development occurs in this hollow, muscular organ. Located behind the urinary bladder, the uterus is no bigger than a small fist, but can expand in pregnancy to more than twenty times in size.

Cervix The narrowing or neck at the base of the uterus, it prevents bacteria from entering the uterus.

Vagina (birth canal) Made of muscular and elastic fibers, the vagina also expands during childbirth.

External genitalia The protective layers that cover the vagina.

ABDOMINAL VISCERA

In the right hand of this specimen is the liver. In the left hand, the intestines, coiled upon each other as they are in the abdominal cavity. Above the intestines is the stomach, which is connected to the throat by the esophagus.

LAYERING

The dissection of this specimen's legs illustrates the three-dimensional relationship of skin, muscle, nerves, and bone that comprise the lower limbs.

BREASTS

The breasts are composed mainly of fat and glandular tissues that are held in place by ligaments. They contain special glands that produce milk following the birth of a child. A series of ducts within the breasts carry milk from the glands to the nipples.

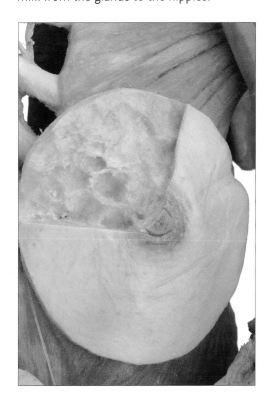

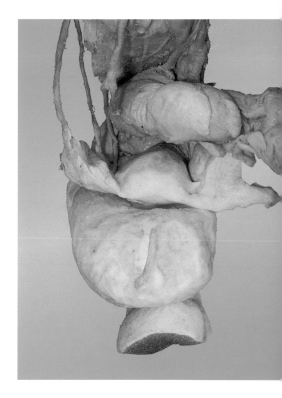

PLACENTA

The placenta forms within the wall of the uterus during pregnancy. It supplies the developing embryo and fetus with oxygen and nutrients, and absorbs fetal waste products.

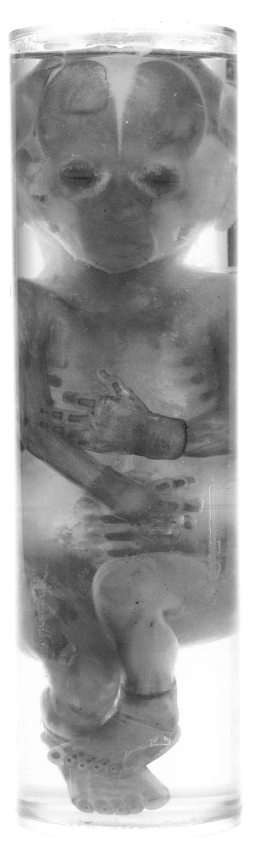

FETAL DEVELOPMENT

Fetal development lasts approximately forty weeks. After implantation, the development of the embryo is rapid and at eleven weeks all of the major organs have been formed. It is at this point that the embryois called a fetus.

MALE REPRODUCTIVE SYSTEM

The male reproductive system includes the penis; the testes, which produce sperm and male hormones; plus several ducts and glands that convey sperm and create semen.

TESTES

Two oval organs contained in the scrotum, the testes create sperm, the male sex cell essential to reproduction. The testes best produce sperm at two degrees below body temperature.

PENIS

The penis contains three cylinders of spongy erectile tissue, which fill with blood when the male becomes aroused. The urethra passes through the penis transporting urine and seminal fluids out of the body.

PROSTATE AND BLADDER

The prostate, visible in the center of this specimen, encircles the urethra at the base of the bladder. It produces an alkaline solution that enables sperm to live within the female reproductive system. In older men, the prostate often becomes enlarged, leading to difficulty with urination.

The urinary bladder, located above and to the right of the prostate, stores urine. Our bladders can hold approximately 1.5 pints (600 milliliters). Pressure receptors in the bladder alert the brain as the bladder fills. If a bladder reaches two-thirds capacity, the urge to empty it is conveyed to the brain.

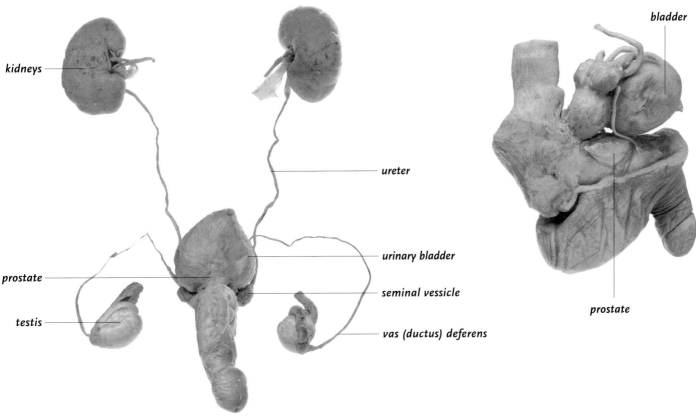

kidneys

ureter

prostate

urinary bladder

seminal vessicle

testis

vas (ductus) deferens

bladder

prostate

KIDNEY AND URETER

Each kidney has a ureter that runs to the urinary bladder. Ureters move urine into the bladder by muscular contractions.

WHOLE KIDNEY AND CORONAL SECTION

The key organs of the urinary system, the kidneys filter over 3 pints (1.0 liter) of blood per minute, removing waste products and creating urine in the process. During your lifetime, you will create 12,000 gallons (45,000 liters) of urine.

CIRCULAT SYSTEM

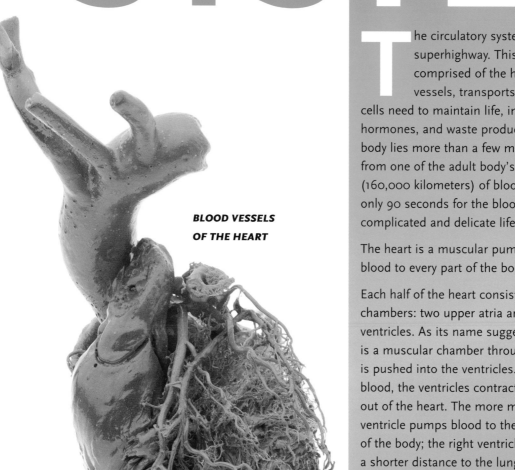

**BLOOD VESSELS
OF THE HEART**

The circulatory system is our body's superhighway. This closed ring, comprised of the heart and blood vessels, transports everything our cells need to maintain life, including nutrients, hormones, and waste products. No cell in the body lies more than a few millimeters away from one of the adult body's 100,000 miles (160,000 kilometers) of blood vessels. It takes only 90 seconds for the blood to transit this complicated and delicate life-giving system.

The heart is a muscular pump that sends blood to every part of the body.

Each half of the heart consists of two chambers: two upper atria and two lower ventricles. As its name suggests, the atrium is a muscular chamber through which blood is pushed into the ventricles. Once filled with blood, the ventricles contract, forcing blood out of the heart. The more muscular left ventricle pumps blood to the far reaches of the body; the right ventricle pumps blood a shorter distance to the lungs.

The coronary arteries, the first branches of the aorta, carry oxygenated blood to the heart muscle. This insures that the heart receives its nourishment before any other organ. When blood flow to the coronary arteries is compromised, the heart is affected. We know this as a heart attack.

THAT TICKING SOUND

The sound you hear when your heart beats does not come from the heart moving; it is the sound of the heart's valves closing.

ORY

BLOOD VESSEL NETWORK

KIDNEYS

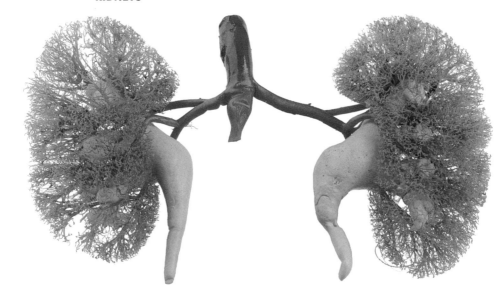

LUNGS

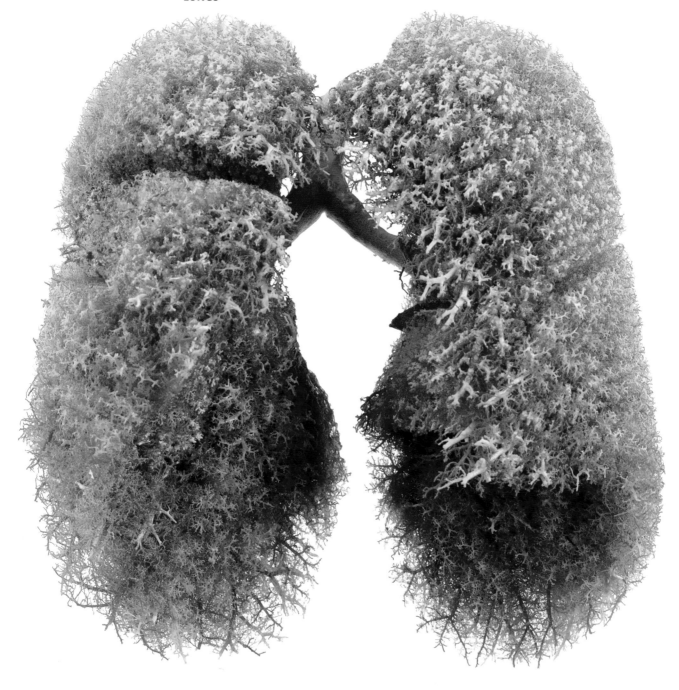

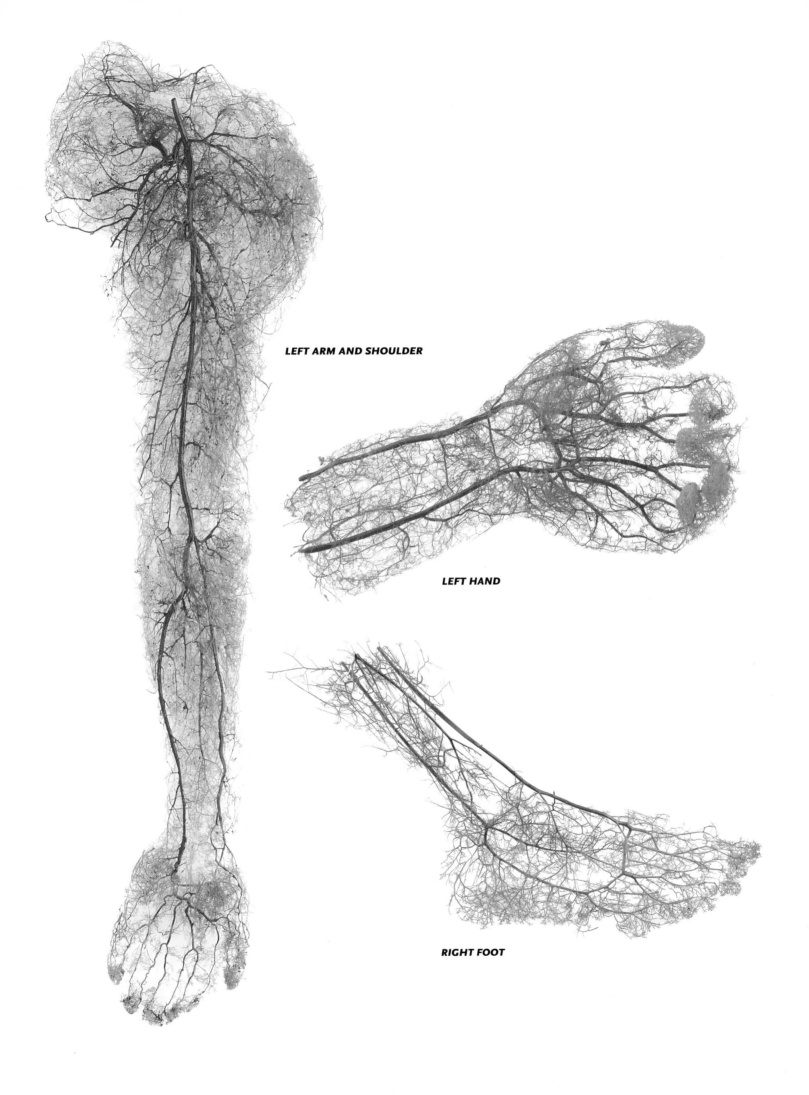

LEFT ARM AND SHOULDER

LEFT HAND

RIGHT FOOT

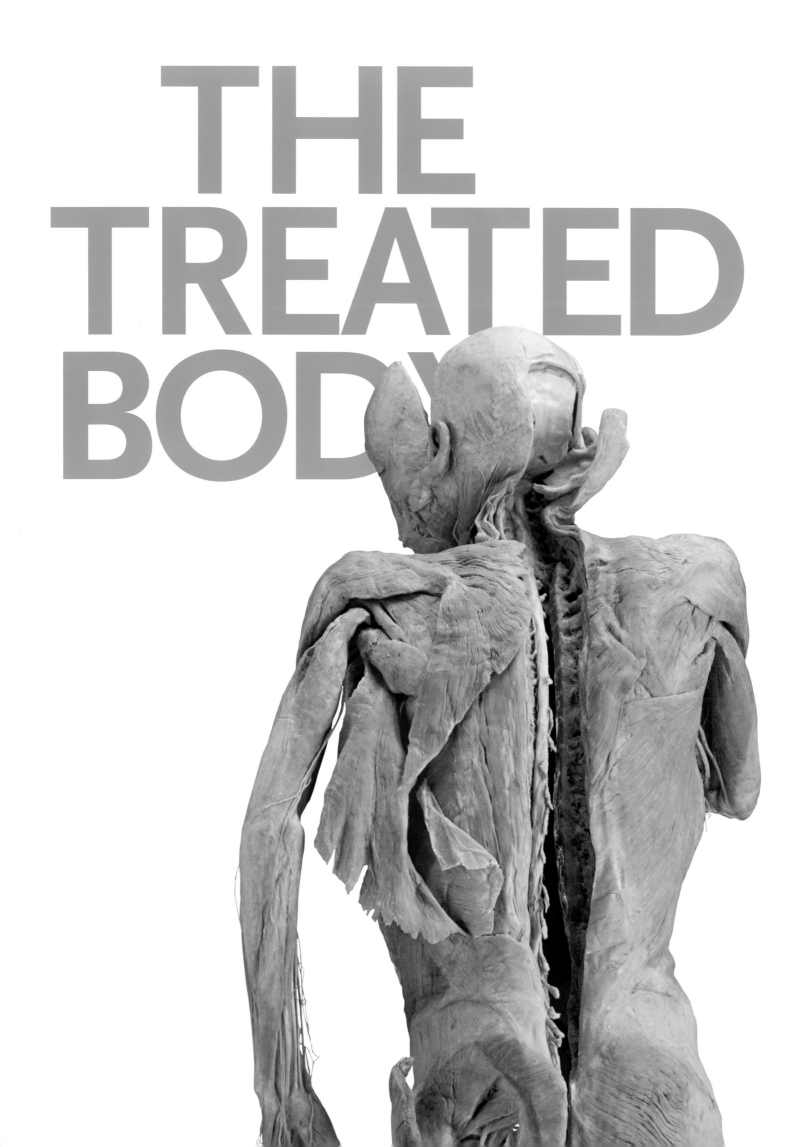

THE
TREATED
BODY

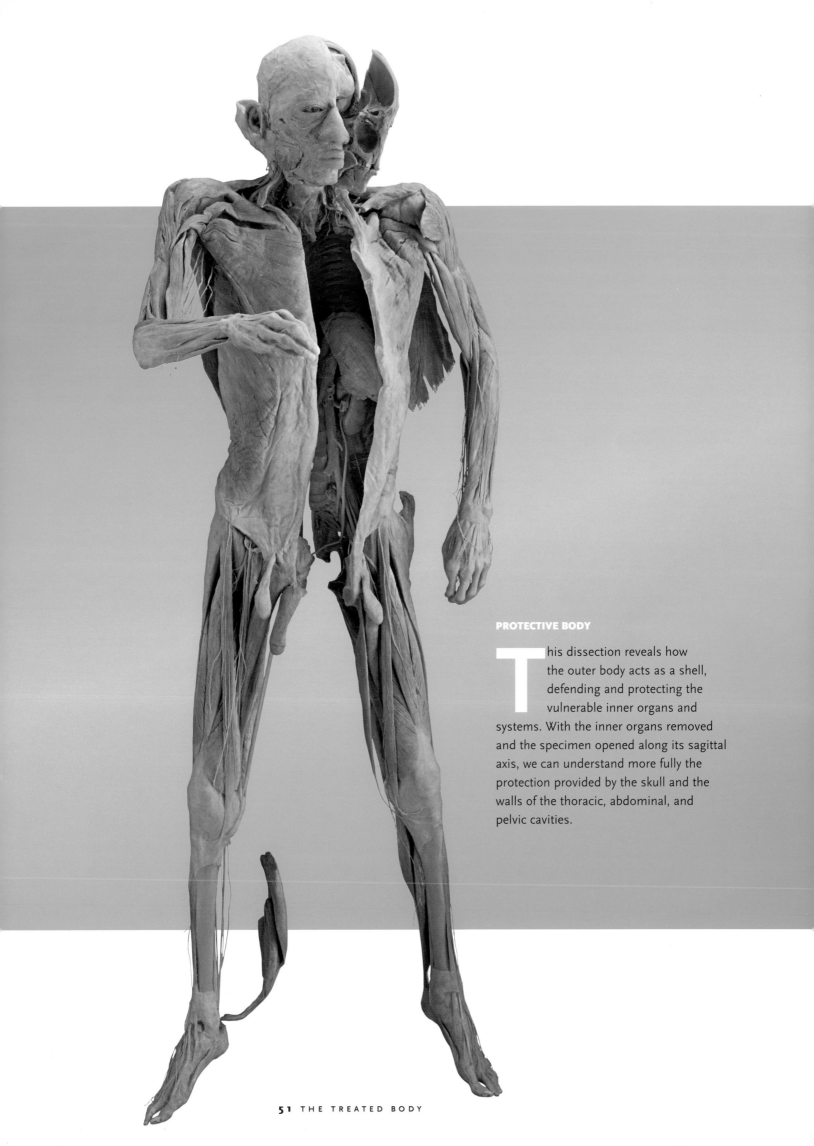

PROTECTIVE BODY

This dissection reveals how the outer body acts as a shell, defending and protecting the vulnerable inner organs and systems. With the inner organs removed and the specimen opened along its sagittal axis, we can understand more fully the protection provided by the skull and the walls of the thoracic, abdominal, and pelvic cavities.

OPERATIVE OPENINGS

Modern surgical techniques can repair almost any injury to our bodies. Several of the openings on the right side of this specimen illustrate the incisions made for routine and emergency surgery. These include shoulder surgery, repair to a compound fracture, hip replacement, and appendix removal. The incision in the stomach is a common point of entry for gastric surgery.

The incisions made on the right side of this specimen follow the Langer's lines within the skin. These lines, named after the doctor who discovered them, form the network of connective tissue that holds skin together. When surgeons make incisions parallel to these lines, skin heals more quickly, with much less scarring. As you can see from the varied angles of each of the incisions, Langer's lines run in different directions on different parts of the body.

The midline of the chest is the place incised for open-heart surgery. In the past, cardiac surgeons cut into the cartilage connecting the sternum (breastbone) to the ribs, or, split the sternum itself. Now, however, the incision is made through the ribs rather than through the sternum, as the bone in ribs mends faster than the costal cartilage. Once the incision has been made for open-heart surgery, the rib cage is opened like a book.

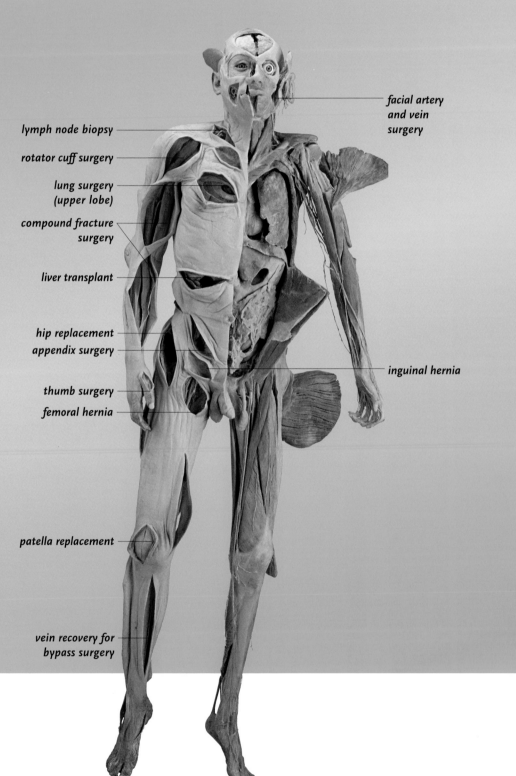

lymph node biopsy

rotator cuff surgery

lung surgery
(upper lobe)

compound fracture
surgery

liver transplant

hip replacement

appendix surgery

thumb surgery

femoral hernia

patella replacement

vein recovery for
bypass surgery

facial artery
and vein
surgery

inguinal hernia

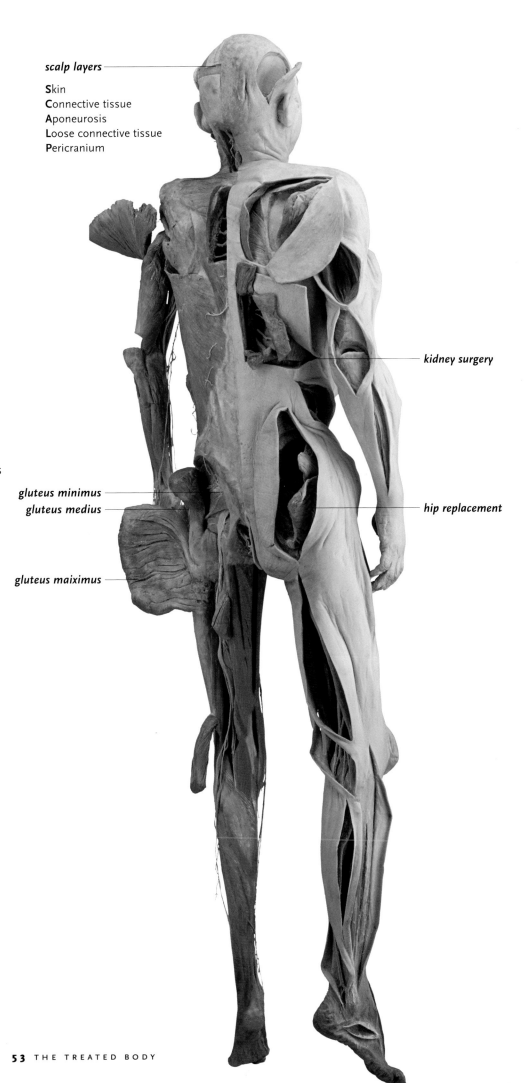

scalp layers

Skin
Connective tissue
Aponeurosis
Loose connective tissue
Pericranium

The dissections on the back of this specimen indicate the sites for surgery of the neck and back. Sections of skin and muscle have been removed to give a better view of the spine and surrounding tissue. Surgeons must use extreme caution when operating in this area, paying special attention to the spinal nerves that emanate from between each vertebra.

The incision towards the right side of the back is often made for kidney surgery. Entering from the back not only gives the surgeon immediate access to the kidney, but also provides a lower risk of damage to surrounding organs.

kidney surgery

gluteus minimus
gluteus medius

hip replacement

gluteus maiximus

MEDICAL PROSTHESIS, PACEMAKER, AND SURGICAL TOOLS

This specimen illustrates the placement of a pacemaker and indicates the various techniques used to heal or replace damaged bones, as well as the surgical tools (spreaders) that assist these techniques.

Bone has the amazing ability to mend itself when broken. Optimal healing occurs when bones are placed in their original positions. For this reason, surgeons often use plates and screws to stabilize broken bones, keeping them fixed in place as they heal. This specimen had plates and screws implanted in the skull and jaw, as well as in the thigh and shin, following fractures to these areas. The metal shafts deep in the thigh and shin provide a template for shattered bones to reconnect. Surgeons access the area by use of a muscle spreader.

Severely broken bones require continued maintenance as they heal. In this case, surgeons employ stabilizers, like those on the wrist and ankle, which use traction to keep bones pressed together.

JOINT REPLACEMENT

Due to disease, or a lifetime of use, the articular cartilages at the ends of the bone sometimes deteriorate. In this case, a prosthesis (artificial replacement) is needed. Made of stainless steel, titanium, or Teflon, the new joint is cemented into the bone, taking the place of the defective one.

Attempting to lengthen the term of an effective implant, researchers are now making joints from ceramics, which do not corrode like metal. Many implants have a honeycomb as part of their design. This arrangement of open spaces is coated with bone cells to help the artificial joint bond more securely to the existing bone.

PACEMAKER

Sometimes the heart's internal pacemaker fails, although the heart muscle remains healthy. In these cases, an external pacemaker, placed under the skin on the right side of the chest, is used to supply the heart with the stimulus needed to continue its beating.

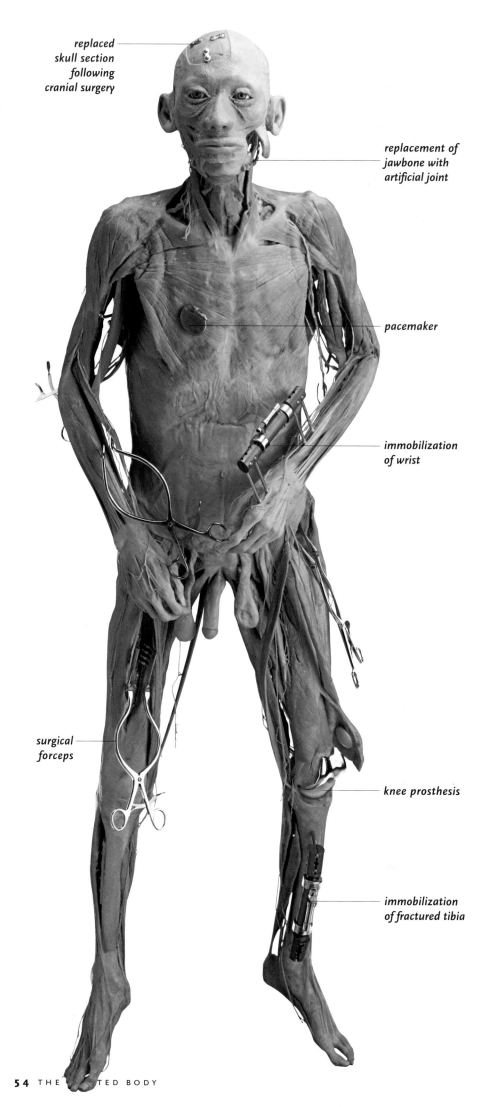

replaced skull section following cranial surgery

replacement of jawbone with artificial joint

pacemaker

immobilization of wrist

surgical forceps

knee prosthesis

immobilization of fractured tibia

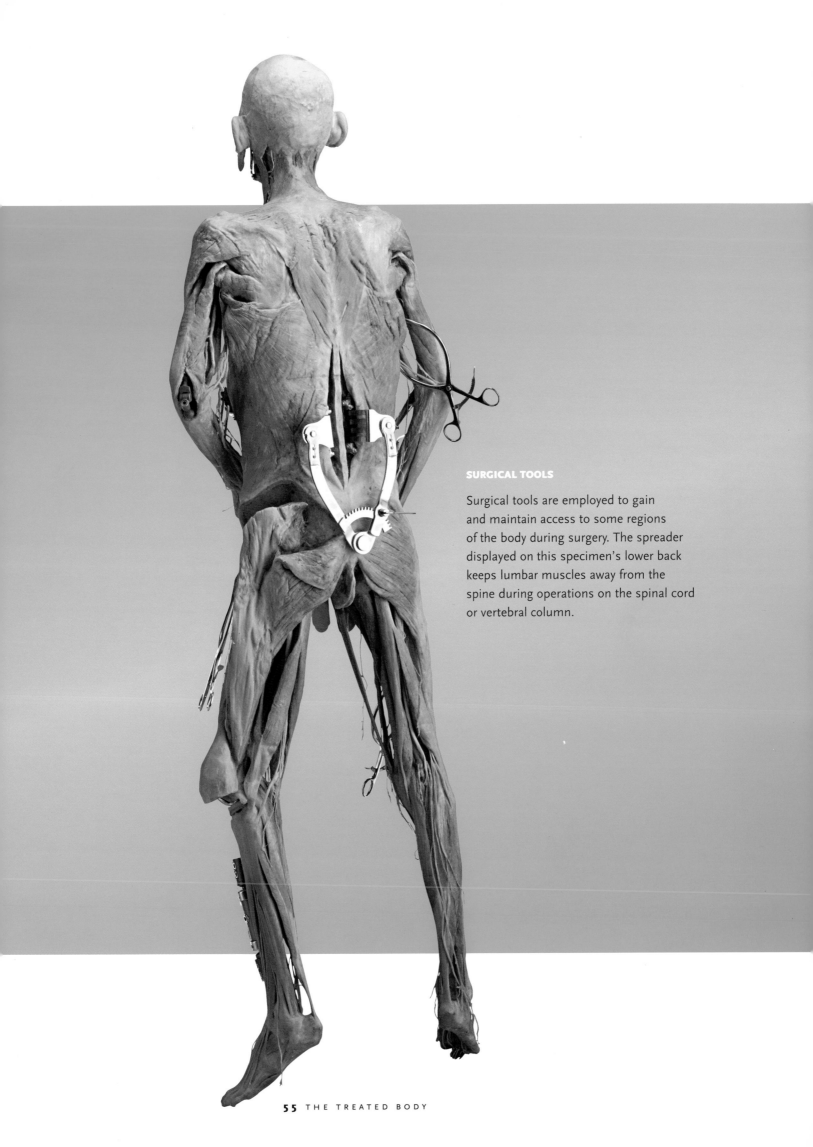

SURGICAL TOOLS

Surgical tools are employed to gain
and maintain access to some regions
of the body during surgery. The spreader
displayed on this specimen's lower back
keeps lumbar muscles away from the
spine during operations on the spinal cord
or vertebral column.

We live in a world surrounded by technology, information, and cement; fast-paced living with no time for reflection. We become ill and expect the physician to heal us swiftly, so we can return to our hectic lives.

When the illness is severe or our mortality comes into question, we may take the time to stop and ponder our existence. But cured, we are off again, not thinking about the extraordinarily, complicated human beings that we are.

Our bodies are an intricately developed machine, more complex and wondrous than all the computers and gadgetry that surround us today. Yet many of us do not really know what lies beneath our skin—how our bodies function, what they need to survive, what destroys them, what revives them.

Bodies Revealed is an attempt to remedy this set of circumstances. Take the knowledge gained from this Exhibition, expand on it, and use it to become a participant in your own health care.

This involves more than improving your diet or beginning a long overdue exercise program. It involves partnering with your doctor to understand what you—and your unique body— need to sustain a full and rewarding life.

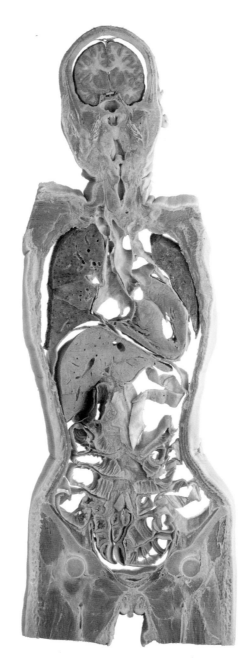
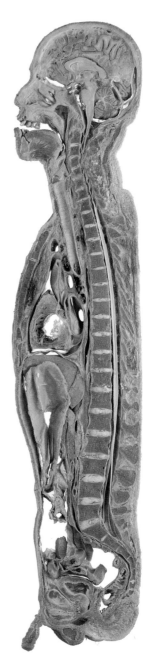